THE HISTORY OF HAIR

THE HISTORY OF HAIR

**An Illustrated Review Of Hair Fashions For Men
Throughout The Ages...**

PLUS A COMPLETE GUIDE TO HAIR CARE FOR MEN

**BY ANN CHARLES
AND ROGER DeANFRASIO**

BONANZA BOOKS·NEW YORK

This edition published by Bonanza Books,
a division of Crown Publishers, Inc.,
by arrangement with the Authors.
a b c d e f g h

DEDICATION

To M.B.A.

ABOUT THE AUTHORS

Ann Charles, the Director of Coiffure Masculine, is a leading authority on historic hairstyles for men. Miss Charles, who first became interested in historic hairstyles when she was studying Costume Design at Hunter College, gives an accurate account of hairstyles for men throughout the ages. In addition, she provides a detailed description of the barbering profession—one of the most complete studies of its kind.

Roger, the famous French hairstylist for men in New York, has won international acclaim as an outstanding leader in his profession. His creative ability in the art of hairstyling, as well as his professional know-how, has gained him recognition in newspapers and magazines throughout the world. As a trendsetter in the field, he has appeared on numerous television shows in an effort to promote the entire industry. Roger, who runs a men's hairstyling salon at 54 East 58th Street in New York, provides practical pointers in the Complete Guide To Hair Care For Men.

ACKNOWLEDGEMENTS

We wish to express our sincere appreciation to Ann and Victor Seader for their encouragement.

In addition, we would like to thank *Men's Hairstylist & Barber's Journal* for their excellent photographs. A special note of thanks is also given to Gene Andrewski, who put his valuable movie collection at our disposal, and to John Verdura, for his many artistic contributions.

PREFACE

Between the sloven and the coxcomb, there is generally a competition—WHICH shall be the more contemptible; the one in the total neglect of everything which might make his appearance more public supportable, and the other, in the cultivation of every superfluous ornament. The former offends by his negligence and dirt, and the latter by his finery and perfumery. Each entertains a supreme contempt for the other, and while both are right in their opinion, both are wrong in their practice. It is not in either extreme that the man of real elegance and refinement will be shown, but in the happy medium which allows taste and judgement to preside over the wardrobe and toilet, while it prevents too great an attention to either, and never allows personal appearance to become the leading object of life.
The Gentlemen's Book of Etiquette, 1860.

INTRODUCTION

THE HISTORY OF HAIR is an Illustrated Review of Hair Fashions For Men Throughout The Ages. It emphasizes hair as a means of personal adornment, and includes a detailed study of the barbering profession.

In addition, it contains a Complete Guide To Hair Care For Men, which covers such subjects as, Finding The Right Hairstyle, Beards, Moustaches, And Sideburns, Maintaining Healthy Hair, Illusion Styling/Hairpieces, Hair Weaving/Hair Transplanting, Hair Straightening/ Permanent Waving, Hair Coloring: Temporary, Semi-Permanent, and Permanent, Men's Cosmetics And Skin Care, Portfolio Of Styles (International Showcase), and Futuristic Predictions.

THE HISTORY OF HAIR should be of interest to any man who has hair. . .or used to have hair. However, it should have special appeal to barbers, students, and stylists already engaged in the profession. It is to these men, that we dedicate this book on the past, present, and future of men's hair fashions.

THE AUTHORS

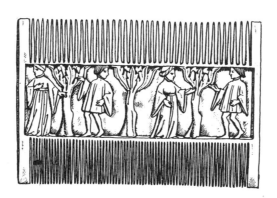

CONTENTS

CHAPTER I
PRIMITIVE TIMES

The Root Of All Evil

In every department of human thought there is present evidence of the persistence of primitive ideas. Scratch the epiderm of the civilized man and the barbarian is found in the derm. Man is the same everywhere at the bottom, if there are many varieties, there is but one species, his civilization is the rare top most shoot of the tree whose roots are in the earth, and whose trunk and larger branches are in savagery - Edward Clodd

A leopard can never change its spots, but a MAN CAN! His desire for decoration is as basic as life, itself. He, too, wants to bring out the beauty in the beast. Decoration, whether it's in the form of a strategically placed shell, or a highly civilized coiffure, usually starts at the top. Hair, if we are to believe what anthropologists tell us, is a logical starting point for all human beings in need of a change. In fact, in certain primitive tribes, although a man may be perfectly comfortable prancing around in the nude, he'd die of embrassment if you caught him with hair down. For example, although the mop-headed Papuans frizz their hair three feet high above their heads, the amount of clothing they wear would make even Lady Godiva blush.

LEFT: FRIZZED HAIRSTYLES, as worn by The Governor's Servants, Port Moresby, New Guinea. The American Museum of Natural History.

THE FIRST MAN-LIKE CREATURE. Pithecanthropus Erectus. Head and Skull Restorations by McGregor.

Originally, man came into this world with more hair than he could handle. It not only covered his head, but the rest of his body, too! The first man-like creature had huge jaws, a low forehead, and a fuzzy frame. The fact is, he was exceedingly ugly, and it was only until he realized his ugliness, that he decided to do something about it.

The earliest type of man-like creature was the Pithecanthropus erectus, or erect ape man. This creature lived about 500,000 years ago in the pliocene or pre-glacial period. Although this specimen walked erect, he looked more like a gorilla, than he did a modern man. Chances are, he worried very little about his coiffure. Like the majority of mammals, he was covered with coarse hair from head to toe. The hair of original man was supposedly colored to match his surroundings.

During the Neolithic or Stone Age (10,000 BC), men made lavish use of ornaments. Necklaces made from teeth, claws, bones, shells, and stones hung around their necks. Both sexes wore their hair fairly long, and small combs made of boxwood, reveal that they, too, were somewhat concerned with the care of the hair.

LEFT: PREHISTORIC HAIRSTYLES. Pithecanthropus Alalus. The American Museum of Natural History.

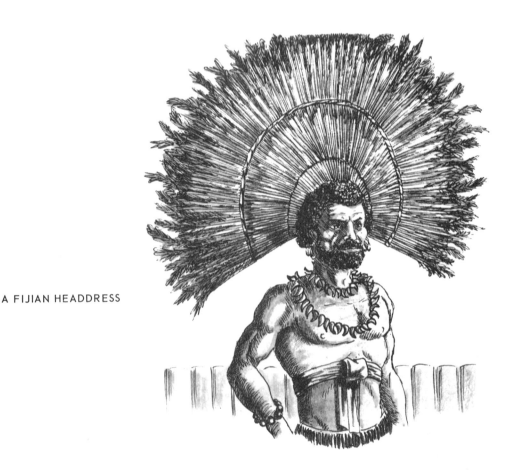

A FIJIAN HEADDRESS

Dandies are about as common among the uncivilized, as they are among the civilized. In the Fiji Islands, for example, dressing the hair was a dandy's delight! As the adventuresome Captain Wilkes once explained it, "In the process of dressing the hair, it is well annointed with oil and mixed with a carbonaceous black until it is completely saturated. The barber then takes the hair pin, which is a long and slender ruch made of tortoise shell or bone, and proceeds to twitch almost every separate hair; this causes it to frizzle and stand erect. The bush of hair is then trimmed smooth by singeing it until it has the appearance of an immense wig. When this has been finished, a piece of tapa, so fine as to resemble tissue paper, is wound in light folds around it, to protect the hair from dew or dust. This covering, when taken care of, will last anywhere from three weeks to one month."

According to one source, "The barber's duty was considered so sacred a matter, that his hands were tabooed from all other employment. In fact, he was not even allowed to feed himself." To dress the hair of a chief took several hours. Therefore, anywhere from two to twelve barbers were on hand to create these elaborate coiffures.

LEFT: DRESSED HAIR . . . Fijian style.

UNISEX HAIRSTYLES, as worn by two Fijians

PRIMITIVE DANDIES

Not satisfied with just twisting and teasing, the Fijians went one step further by dyeing their mop-like hair red, white, blue, or yellow. The younger men were known to favor flaxen and crimson shades.

The natives of Duke of York's Island have also favored hair of different colors. But rather than dye it, they smeared it with grease and sprinkled it afterwards with a white, red, or yellow powder made of burnt shells and coral.

Some of the greatest dandies, however, were the Griquas, who smeared themselves with grease and red ochre, while the head was annointed with a blue pomatum made of mica. The particles of shinning mica falling on the body were considered highly ornamental, and the natives viewed the mixture of colors as very attractive.

In Africa, even today, it is not uncommon to see a tribesman wearing a snowy white cap made from plaster of clay mixed with bleach. When finished, this mixture produces a startling mop of toast-colored wool. A light quill or beaded blue butterfly usually accents the zig-zag fibres.

ABOVE: FRIZZED HAIR, as worn by a modern dandy. Fashions by Mr. Fish. Photo: Kenn Duncan.

AN AMERICAN INDIAN wearing facial paint and ornate headdress.

AN AMERICAN INDIAN wearing facial paint and ornate headdress.

NOÁPEH

The Indians of Oregon, at least in the time of Captain Cook's first voyage, used a red cosmetic, probably ordinary wet clay,,as their only adornment. In addition, *Captain Cook's Journal* reports, "The majority of the men and some of the women of the Friendly Isles, whose hair was by nature thick, straight, and black, wore it dyed orange, brown, or purple, and many, in addition to tinting, curled or frizzed it. One man, Cook tells us, wore a large feather through his nose.

CONE HEADDRESSES

No part of the human body has been more manipulated than hair. Among Dyak men, it was a common practice to grow the back hair long and shave the front hair. The natives of Borneo shaved the entire scalp, except for a large tuft of long hair which hung down the back.

All hair, except on the crown of the head, was detested by the Amazon Indians. The Dyaks of Borneo have even been known to pluck out not only their eyebrows, but their eyelashes, too. The New Zealanders have rarely worn beards, as they plucked out the hairs with a pair of mussel shells or pincers, as soon as they appeared.

Captain Cook, when he visited the Sandwich Islanders, described their hair as, "naturally black, but dyed brown, and mostly worn cropped short; others wore it long and flowing, or tied in a bunch."

The Dinkas have been known to dye their hair red, whereas the Djibbas, a warlike people, prided themselves in interweaving the hair of their victims with their own, forming a thick tail. The length of the tail indicated one's valour.

Captain Leechey in his voyages to Behring's Strait, stated that the hair of the Indians and natives of the quarter was done up in large plaits on each side of the head, and the edges of the eyelids were blackened with plumbago, rubbed with a little saliva upon a piece of slate.

William Schouten, in his voyage to the Polynesian Isles revealed that the inhabitants of Horn Island, "wore their hair, some combed, some frizzled, some tied up in knots, and some had it standing bolt upright, like hog bristles. The king and some of his courtiers had very long locks hanging down below their hips, bound up with a knot or two, but the women were all cropped close."

LEFT: BEARDED MAN, as seen in Prehistoric Mexican Sculpture. Courtesy of The Museum of Primitive Art.

AMERICAN INDIAN HEADDRESS

False hair, too, has been frequently worn by primitive people. Natives on the South of New Guinea, troubled with stubborn hair, nevertheless, admired ringlets as a headdress. Consequently, they cut off the ringlets and twisted them into skull caps, making very compact wigs. The American Indians from New York and New England often fashioned an artificial roach of deers' tail bristles, which was a more luxurious ornament than their natural adornment. Baldness was supposedly unknown among these natives.

With the American Indian, the right to wear a feather in the headdress, had to be won in battle or on the hunting ground. To dress like a brave, one had to qualify as a brave. The great war chiefs of the Marquesses were entitled to wear the tavaha, a huge ceremonial headdress made from at least 250 cocks.

LEFT: THE INFLUENCE OF THE AMERICAN INDIAN, as seen in modern hairstyles. Hairstyle by Roger of New York. Photo: Lowell McFarland. (Courtesy of "Men's Hairstylist & Barber's Journal.")

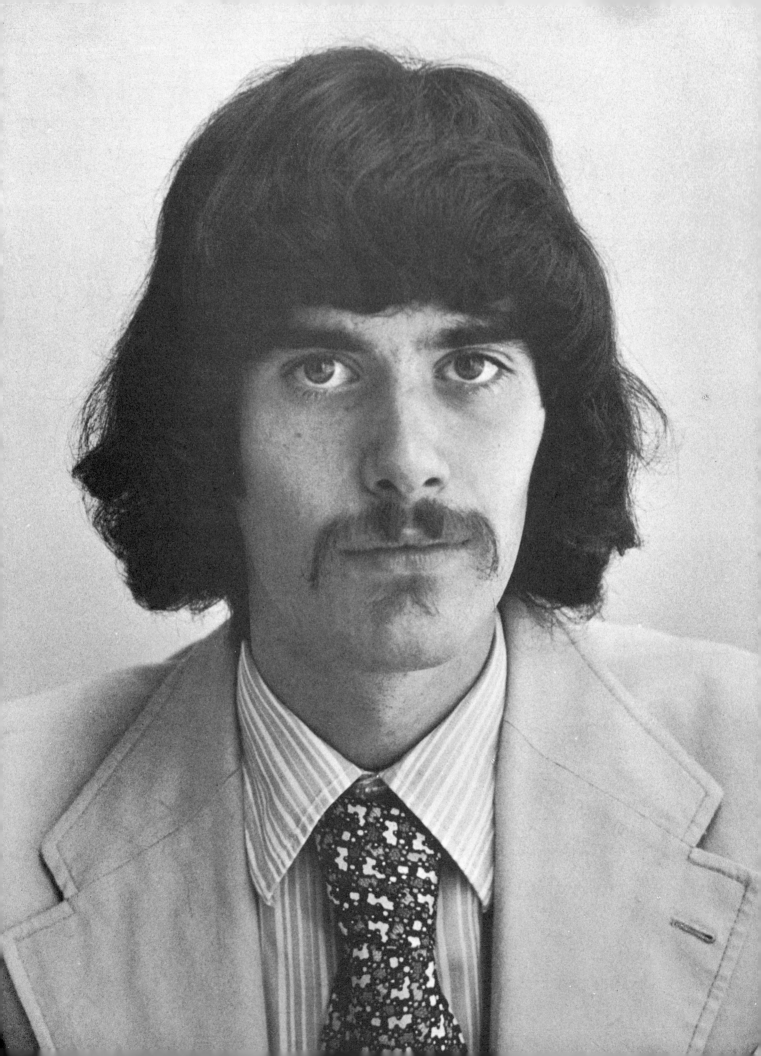

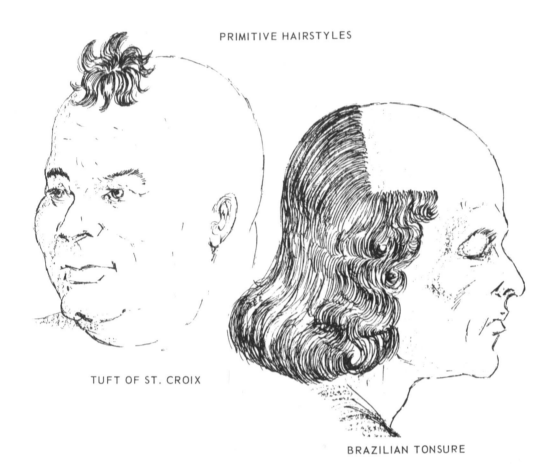

PRIMITIVE HAIRSTYLES

TUFT OF ST. CROIX

BRAZILIAN TONSURE

The care and dressing of hair has always been a primitive pastime. The Polynesians spent a great deal of time washing and shampooing their hair with mouoi, or scented oil. When it was short, they sometimes dressed it with a gummy substance obtained from the trunk of the coconut tree called pia. Another substance obtained from the bread-fruit tree, gave the hair a shiny appearance and fixed it as straight as if it had been stiffened with rosin. The Tahitians greased both the hair and beard with coconut oil.

The natives of the Belgian Congo used castor bean oil for dressing the hair. In addition, many African tribes plastered their hair with mud. The New Zealanders, on the other hand, favored shark's oil, even though it had a most repulsive odor, to beautify the hair.

Among the American Indians, a primitive sort of shampoo made from roots and herbs, was thought highly beneficial to the hair. The brave would take the roots of a special plant, and beat it until it was soft lather. The noble red man then stooped over the bowl, while his squaw played the role of barber.

LEFT: LONG HAIR FOR MEN has been a trend with the civilized, as well as the uncivilized. Photo: Rene Guzman.

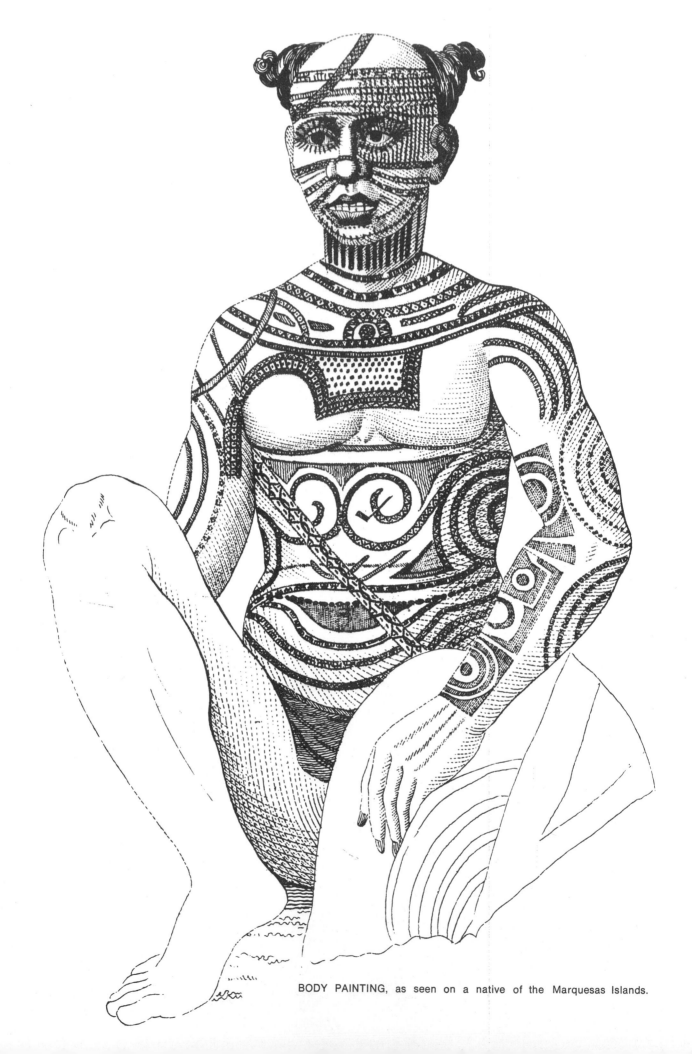

BODY PAINTING, as seen on a native of the Marquesas Islands.

For while it seems to be an almost universal rule of nature that the male is more glorious than the female, in human life, at least in primitive communities, this is also so. Ornaments among the Indians of Guiana were worn more by men, than by women. The stock ornament was painting. A man who wanted to be considered a sharp dresser, would probably coat both his feet a bright red, paint his torso a blue-black, and then add an interesting variety of spots and streaks. A band of color was usually painted along the bridge of his nose, where his eyebrows used to be until he pulled them out.

On the wedding night, the groom of the Koita people, would wear a headdress of cassoway feathers, a red and yellow streaked face, and ears decorated with dried pig tails.

Throughout the entire Australian continent, natives have stained their naked bodies with black, red, yellow, and white paint. Red ochre was usually the fashion favorite. Among the Guaycurus, men painted their bodies half red and half white. In New Zealand, the lips of both sexes were generally dyed blue. As Theophile Gautier once put it, "Having no clothes to embroider, they embroider themselves."

ELABORATE HEADDRESS, as worn by American Indian

The American Indian, too, has been meticulous about his personal grooming. When the first explorers came to America, the red man had reached a highly developed stage in body painting and use of dyes and pigments. According to a certain Mr. Murray in Rimmel's *Book of Perfumes,* "He never saw a dandy to equal him for vanity. He usually commenced his toilet at 8:00 AM, and it wasn't until much later, that he finished."

Tattooing, which may be considered an indelible form of cosmetics, has ranked among the chief personal adornments of the Australians and Polynesians. Many African tribes have marked their bodies with cicatrices, rubbing wood ashes in the wounds on the face and body. This caused the wounds to swell and heal into a purplish color, which was regarded as a mark of distinction. Men so marked were considered more attractive to women than those whose scars were not colored.

LEFT: CURLY HAIR AND MUTTON CHOPS as seen on a native of Australia. Note the body decoration.

ADORNMENT in the form of body painting and frizzed hair.

Adornment can also assume many other forms. Among the Iroquois Indians, oddly enough, fans were a male prerogative. Their fans, woven of grass and large bird feathers, were important fashion accessories. The grass with which the fans were plaited were chosen with special care. Consequently, it wasn't unusual to find a fierce-looking brave fanning himself, as he filled the air with a delicious, grassy perfume.

Among the American Indians, it is further noted, that wild tribes have never cared for heavy perfumes. They have always preferred a light, fleeting fragrance, one which was obtained from the fruits of the meadow in August. Probably, the first perfumes used by the savages were fragrant wild flowers. The natives rubbed their skins with the aromatic blossoms and sweet-smelling juices. There are, according to historians, many cases where men have been more lavish users of perfumes than women. At Nooka-hiva, the principle of the Marquesan Islands, both sexes annointed themselves freely with sweet-scented coconut oil. The most refined men used the juice of the papa, which was supposed to whiten the skin and preserve its smoothness.

The comb, which dates back to the earliest days of civilization, has been used by all people concerned with the care of the hair. Fingers served as the earliest combs, and were superseded by fish bones fastened between pieces of wood. Combs of stone, as well as bone, are found in many of today's museums. These combs, which were used for cleaning and arranging the hair, had only one or two teeth. The American Indian developed combs that had as many as seven teeth. These were usually made from horn.

THE CENTER PART, FEATHERS, AND COMBS, accent this American Indian hairstyle.

NEW ZEALAND TATTOOED HEADS

Besides using combs for their practical value, combs have also been used for decorative purposes. American Indians used combs to fasten their hair into various styles. Combs of palm wood and grass decorated with small feathers accented these primitive hairstyles. The Australian aborigines decorated their hair with opossum tails and kangaroo teeth. The hair of the New Zealanders, when it was allowed to grow long, was held in place by elaborately carved wooden combs. Chignons of monkey fur were also worn by the most fashionable men.

Man's concern for his hair is not only confined to the living. Even among the dead, decorated heads take on great importance. Embalming, which was practiced by New Zealanders, was confined to the heads of cherished relatives. After taking out the brains, the heads were stuffed with flowers, baked in ovens, and finally dried in the sun. These heads were kept in carefully made baskets, scented with oil. They were brought out only on special occasions, at which time, the entire family would cry over them.

CHAPTER II
THE ANCIENT EGYPTIANS

King Tut's Toilet

The custom of dyeing hair dates back to Ancient Egyptian times when the mother of the first King of Egypt distinguished herself by inventing a dye to restore color. An Egyptian manuscript dated 1200 BC suggests "dried tadpoles from the canal crushed in oil" and a combination of "tortoise shell and babgu bird boiled in oil." In the highly sophisticated period after 1150 BC, wigs of red, green, and blue, were worn by men. Both henna and indigo were used as hair dyes.

In addition to dyes, the Egyptians also invented formulas for falling hair and pomades to strengthen hair. For falling hair, one Ancient Egyptian formula prescribed, "a mixture of six kinds of fat—the fat of a hippopotamus, a lion, a cat, a crocodile, a snake, and an ibex." For strengthening the hair, the "tooth of a donkey crushed in oil" suposedly worked miracles.

Throughout the Egyptian era, wigs were highly fashionable. Wigs were made of human hair, black sheep's wool or palm leaf fibres dyed black. The hair was attached to a woven porous foundation which provided ventilation.

LEFT: FALSE BEARD, as seen on King Tut's Coffin. The Metropolitan Museum of Art. Photo: Harry Burton.

BEARD, as seen on the Sphinx of Queen Hatshepsut. The Metropolitan Museum of Art.

Does this mean I've been impeached?

Wigs, which were frequently used in religious feasts and ceremonies, were done up in various styles: the short, square cut, fringes and lengthening at the back, and the classical, dynasty wigs. These wigs, which were placed on stands after wearing, were usually dressed by slaves. At first, the very short bob-like wigs were worn by the upper classes. This style was later adopted by the commoners. The people of rank then turned to longer and more elaborate wigs. Very often, the natural hair of the laborer was cut in a short bob, or he wore no covering at all. In general, wigs were worn by nobility, officers of rank, and the wealthy.

Beards, mostly false, were also worn by men of rank. The rank of the individual was signified by the length of the beard. The beard of an individual rank was short and square. The beard of a king was equally square, but much longer. The beard of a god was pointed and turned up at the end. Inasmuch as Pharaohs were regarded as gods after death, they, too, were depicted with curved beards. Merchants, land owners, and upper classes wore beards. The false beards were made of tufts of hair held in place by cords looped back over the ears. Slaves and lower classes were smooth-shaven.

The plaited beard was often worn by queens. It was held in place by a ribbon tied in back under the wig, or attached to a gold chin strap. Statues of Hatshepsut show her wearing a long, turned up beard.

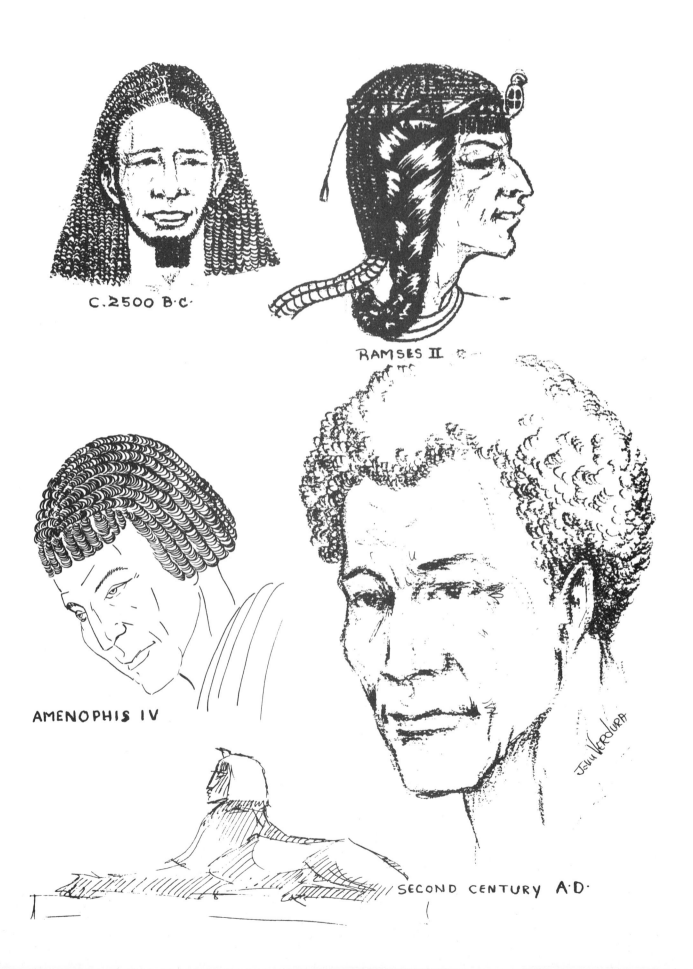

C. 2500 B.C.

RAMSES II

AMENOPHIS IV

SECOND CENTURY A.D.

Jonn Verdura

CARTER EXAMINING THE TOMB OF KING TUT-ANKH-AMUN.

Egyptian men painted their eyebrows and all around the eyes with antimony, malachite, and a black powder called kohl. Kohl was used to blacken the edge of the eyelids both above and below the eye. The kohl was applied with a small probe of wood, ivory, or silver, which tapered to a blunt edge.

The Egyptians have also been known to stain their hands and feet with the juice of henna leaves. The result was a yellowish red or deep orange color. It was a common practice to dye the tops of the fingers and toes as far as the first joints. The dyeing was renewed every fortnight. This interest in treating the nails is evidenced by an Ancient Egyptian tomb which depicts a pedicurist attending to a man's toes.

Perfume was also very popular among Egyptian men. In early times, the aromatics were used only for religious ceremonies and embalming. However, the Egyptians gradually carried them over into their daily life. Inscriptions on Egyptian tombs tell us that people were required to perfume themselves at least once a week.

Precious perfumes were usually purchased from the priests who prepared them in their own laboratories. The unguents varied from myrrh to frankincense to bitter almond. A strange custom indulged in when banqueting was the wearing of an ornamental cone of perfumed fat on top of the head or wig. As the party progressed, the cone melted and the perfume ran down over the person.

According to Egyptian custom, no king could be crowned without first being annointed with perfumed oils. When King Tutankhamun's tomb was opened in the 1920s, cosmetic jars, in spite of their being buried for 3,000 years, still retained their sweet fragrance.

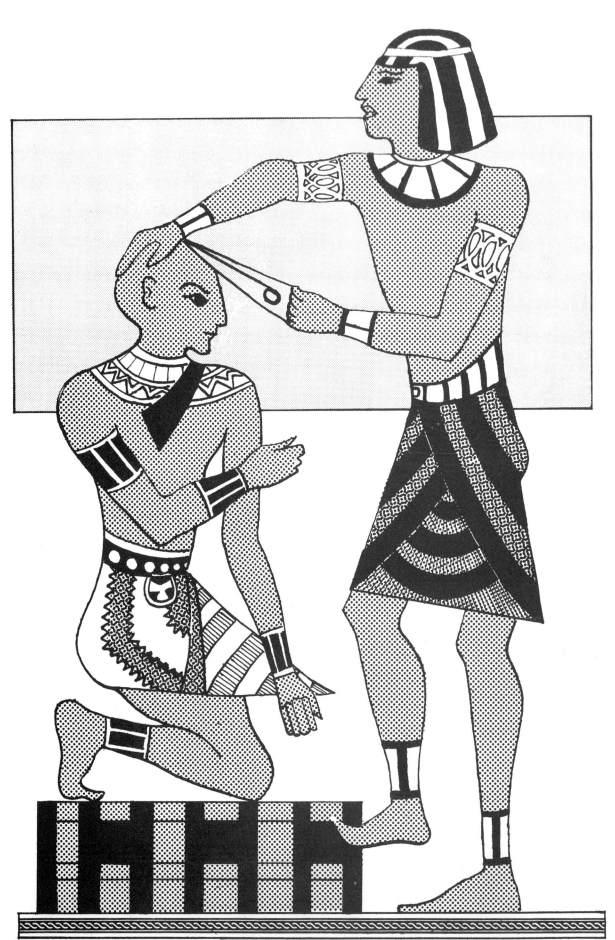

AN EGYPTIAN BARBER giving a haircut. Note the wig which the barber is wearing, and the shaved head of the customer.

SHAVED HEAD, as seen on Egyptian wall painting. Tomb of Apuy, 1250 B.C. The Metropolitan Museum of Art.

With all this emphasis on good grooming, it's no wonder that the barber was held in high esteem. At the Haskell Oriental Museum in Chicago, may be seen an architrane from the Tomb of Khabauptah, chief hairdresser and manicurist of the Pharaoh. (Never a she is mentioned, nor are there any references to lady hairdressers — only men.)

Ancient records indicate barber businesses and barber gods. Although wealthy clients received daily visits from their barber each morning, the poorer class depended upon a traveling barber who usually set up his stool under a tree. Hairs that defied the razor were just pulled out. The razors, which looked like large wooden chisels, were carried in open-mouthed baskets.

Other Ancient civilizations, such as, the Assyrians, the Babylonians, the Persians, and the Jews, were greatly concerned with the care of the hair.

The Assyrian monarch dressed his long beard with fastidious care. His whiskers were arranged in tiny curls. His moustache, which was cut off above the lip, was similarly curled at the corners of the mouth. Numerous and regular curls covered his cheeks, and the part of his beard which hung down, was divided into tightly twisted curls broken by three horizontal rows of curls, and three similar rows were found again at the bottom. This arrangement was more or less systematically carried out, in all males.

The wigs worn by the Assyrians were smaller and shaped differently that those of the Egyptians. The crimped hair, whether real or false, was usually parted in the center, pulled back behind the ears, and allowed to hang down onto the shoulders. Ends were often tightly curled. Curling irons or tongs were in common use. During special occasions, the hair was powdered with gold dust or scented with pulverized yellow starch. The masculine beard was given the same attention. Ointments were applied to the hair, and the Assyrians reportedly, had a black dye for eyebrows, beard, and hair. A description of the Assyrian toilet is revealed in the story of Parsondes. On Nararus upbraiding Parsondes for his ingratitude he replied, "Am I Not more manly and more useful to the king than you are—who are shaved and have your eyes underlined with stibium and your face painted with a white lead?"

LEFT: THE CLEAN-SHAVEN LOOK, as seen on Head of Gudea, Governor of Lagash. The Metropolitan Museum of Art.

THE LEGEND OF SAMSON AND DELILAH — According to the legend, Samson, a judge in Israel was robbed of his strength, when Delilah betrayed him by cutting off his hair. The above mural is from the salon of Samson and Delilah in London, England.

The upper class Babylonians, about the middle of the third millenium, had long hair which was kept in place by bands of gold. Rosettes were often soldered to the bands. Their beards which were set with tree gum were perfumed and elaborately arranged. In the 7th century BC, King Assurbanipal supposedly favored the use of cheek rouge. In addition, perfume was widely used among fashionable young men.

The Persian men, following the tradition of the Assyrians and Babylonians stained their hair and beards orange-red. Heavy eyebrows were a sign of beauty, especially if they met over the nose, and both men and women drew in the line with kohl.

Although the Hebrews were forbidden to shave, there have been frequent references to razors. The Israelites, who preferred black hair, used hair dyes, as well as perfumed oils. Baldness was considered not only a defect, but a curse. The prophets often figuratively applied it as a denunciation of judgments. Thus Isaiah observes that "Instead of well-set hair, there shall be baldness. And shame shall be upon all faces and baldness upon all their heads."

At the time of David, hair was considered a great ornament, and the longer it was, the more it was esteemed. To enhance its beauty, it was often powdered with gold dust.

LEFT: LONG, CURLED BEARD, as worn by Ancient Assyrians. Wall painting of Winged Genie. The Metropolitan Museum of Art.

CHAPTER III
THE ANCIENT GREEKS

The Glory That Was Grease

The first tonsorial centers were established by the Greeks. The "tonstrina," as the Greeks called it, was a popular hangout for philosophers and poets. Here's where a budding Plato could have his beard curled, his toenails cut, and his fingernails cleaned. Besides, since many of the barbers were also skilled in massage, calisthenics, and surgery, the client not only had a chance to have his face lifted, but the rest of his body, too.

The local barber shop was the central clearing house for all the latest social, political, and sporting news. Since the Greeks rivaled each other in the excellence of their beards, beard trimming grew into an important art. Consequently, barbers were considered leading citizens of the community. Razors, which were crescent-shaped and rather clumsy to handle, were kept busy at the art until Alexander commanded that all his soldiers be clean-shaven.

Beards were worn by philosophers, poets, and historians. The busts of Zeus and Homer show that full beards were worn in Homeric times. During the Periclean Age, the face was smooth-shaven. However in the Alexandrian Age, a patch of hair was often worn in front of the ears.

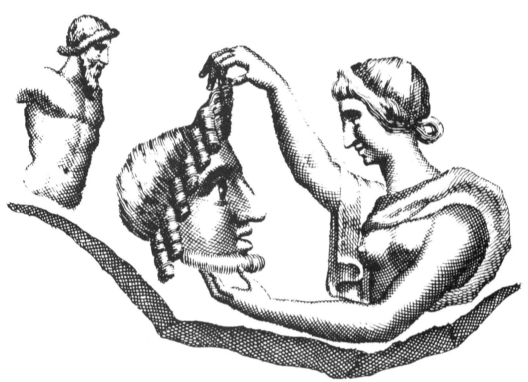

The Greeks, in general, never favored moustaches without beards, as it was considered the mark of a barbarian. Among the early Greeks, hair styles for men and women were very similiar. Later on men wore their hair short and women, long. During the periods when long hair was in fashion, Athenian gentlemen preferred long, rather loose curls. Philosophers were known to wear shoulder-length hair. In fact, at one time, long hair was so general, that the Greeks were distinguished from the barbarians who wore their hair short.

By the end of the sixth century BC, shorter hairstyles were favored. In general, masculine styles varied from spiral curls to ringlets to the short haircut of today. For special effects, men sometimes wore wreaths of flowers in their hair. The greatest luxury of the period was a gold grasshopper which was used to decorate a hairstyle in which the hair was rolled up into a knot. Although hair was often curled, the curls were usually soft rather than stiff, and there were no great distortions in the general shape of the head. Spartan men usually took little pains with their hair, except on the eve of battle, at which time it was carefully arranged. Although natural hair was preferred, some wigs were known. For example, Hannibal had a number of wigs in various styles and colors. In addition, since most Greeks were of dark complexion, fair hair was a sign of beauty. Homer mentions the blonde hair of Achilles.

LEFT: ARISTOTLE CONTEMPLATING THE BUST OF HOMER. By Rembrandt. The Metropolitan Museum of Art.

FIFTH CENTURY B.C.

450 B.C.

330 B.C.

5th CENTURY B.C.

John Verdura

A GREEK DANDY GETTING A SHAVE

Greek dandies, who made lavish use of powders and paints, had perfumes for each portion of the body. There were perfumes to clear befuddled minds; perfumes to cure every illness that human flesh was heir to, and, of course, perfumes that guranteed to win love. Even Diogenes lavishly perfumed his feet saying that it was wasteful to use perfume on one's head, "whence the scent rose benefitting only the birds," whereas by using it on his feet, his whole body was bathed in delightful evaporating odors."

Even the dead were buried with perfumes. A bottle or flask of a man's favorite fragrance was placed in his coffin. Those too poor to inter persons, had a mourner paint a picture of a flask on their caskets.

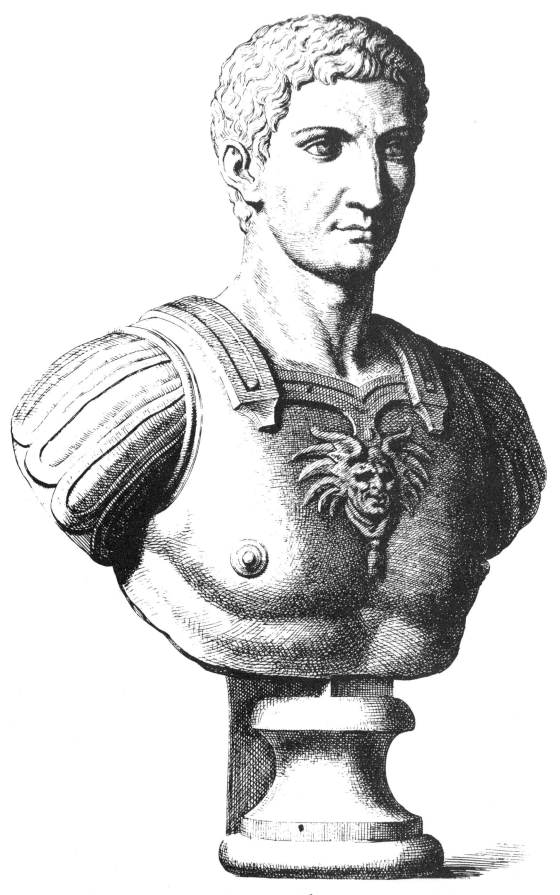

Tiberius.

CHAPTER IV
THE ANCIENT ROMANS

Roamin' Hands And Painted Heads

The Roman dandies relied heavily on paints, perfumes, and patches. Petronius poked fun at a young man whose facial paint had melted in the heat and trickled down to his chin. Both sexes whitened their skin with chalk or white lead. A lip rouge of vegetable dye was also used. Roman men favored milk as a skin beautifier.

According to Pliny, the early Latin naturalist and writer, a blue or greenish tint was used to stain a man's eyelids and underneath the eye. Pliny also describes a formula for making rouge from a Syrian root.

The Romans did not make such universal use of perfume as did the Greeks. However, upon special occasions it was not unusual to have showers of perfume fall from the ceiling onto the guests. The Emperor Otho even carried a supply of perfumes when he was at war. It is said that when Lucious Plotius concealed himself at Salernum, his hiding place was revealed by the fragrance of his perfume.

The Romans not only perfumed their hair, but the rest of their bodies, too. Even the soles of their feet were bathed in sweet-smelling scents. The most elegant men used different perfumes for each part of the body. In addition, they perfumed their clothing, their beds, their walls, their flags, and sometimes, even their horses. Both men and women made use of the beauty spot. These patches were made of soft leather, and the orators were often seen from the tribune wearing same.

Men also dyed their locks. The dyes orignated with the Gauls, who colored their own hair red. The Germans acquired the secret formula, and made up balls of caustic soap, which they exported to Rome.

Pliny tells us about the dye produced by boiled walnut shells and leek parings; of a mixture of oil, ashes, and earthworms to prevent hair from turning white; of crushed myrtle berries to prevent baldness.

False hair, such as toupees; or entire wigs made of goat's skin, were worn by those who could afford the luxury. According to Suetonius, the Roman perruquiers had attained a great deal of proficiency in the art of wigmaking. He tells us that Otho's wig was so beautifully made that it looked perfectly natural. These appendages, however, were very costly at that time, and a certain Phoebus, who had more imagination than ready cash, painted imaginary locks on his head by means of a dark pomatum. As Martial so eloquently put it, "Phoebus belies with oil his absent hairs, and o'er his scalp a painted peruke wears; Thou need'st no barber to dress thy pate, Phoebus; a sponge would better do the feat."

At night, they covered their bald head with bladders. Wigs were occasionally worn by men either as a disguise, or in the case of Hadrian, to conceal baldness. Baldness was considered a deformity among Roman men, and in such cases, a kind of wig was worn made of hair attached to skin.

LEFT: SHORT, FRONTAL FRINGE, as seen on Head of Constantine. The Metropolitan Museum of Art.

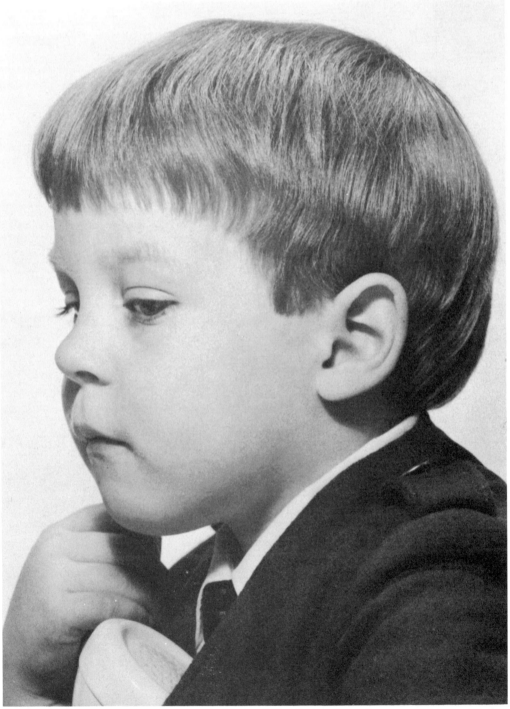

ABOVE: MODERN VERSION OF THE CAESAR CUT. Photo: Kenn Duncan. Hairstyle by Sam Caramanna. (Courtesy of Men's Hairstylist).

In general, the Romans were very fond of light hair. Julius Capitolinus informs us that the Emperor Verus had such a fondness for light hair that in order to keep his own that color, he sprinkled it from time to time, with distilled gold so that it would look more brilliant.

To get the fair-haired look, Ancient formulas recommended "a crow's liver and swallows dung."

LEFT: BUST OF A CHILD. Ancient Roman. The Metropolitan Museum of Art.

Make the part on the left, please

AN ANCIENT ROMAN BARBER SHOP. Painting hair on heads.

THE FIRST ROMAN BARBER.

Shaving was unknown in Rome until about 296 BC when a Sicilian by the name of Vicinius Mena landed in Rome with a troop of beard-happy barbers. The Roman General Scipio of about 234 to 183 BC was the first Roman to shave every day. Scipio's chin, it was recorded, was formerly dressed three times a day.

At first the barbers just cropped beards, but it wasn't long before they went all the way and chopped them all off. Eventually, when the fashion caught on, the Romans showed their enthusiasm by erecting a statue to the first barber of Rome.

The barber would first prepare the client for shaving by softening up the face. The client usually took a steam bath, which not only relaxed him, but also made him hungry and thirsty, as well. To accommodate him even further, the barber usually provided wine, women (female attendants) and food, at an extra fee, of course. Among the services offered were shaving, haircutting, hairdressing, massaging, and manicuring. In addition, cosmetics consisting of rare ointments, were included in the good grooming ritual.

JULIUS CAESAR wearing the laurel wreath.

AN ANCIENT ROMAN BARBER SHOP

The Roman barber shop excelled the Greek barber shop in the respect that the Romans were the first to adopt the practice of warming water in a special vessel for the comfort of their clients. In addition, the flat, straight razors which they used, were far superior to those of their predecessors.

The razor, it is noted, was first introduced into Rome by Tarquinius, the 5th King (616-578 BC) in an effort to bring about some hygenic reform. The Romans did not take quickly to the "effeminate" ways of the Greeks, and it was over a century before shaving began.

The first Imperial, Julius Caesar shaved, as Suetonius tells us. He was, says Suetonius, not only shaved, but plucked—for depilatories were by then in common use among the Roman fops of whom Caesar was a fashionable leader.

ANCIENT ROMAN BATHS — Bathing was a fine art among the Romans. Upon entering a bath, Roman men undressed, giving their clothes to persons hired especially for this purpose. In the unctuarium, they received a dosing of inexpensive perfumes and oils. This was followed by a cold bath, and then a hot bath, at which time, they scrubbed themselves with scented oils.

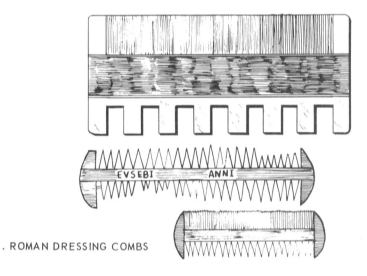

. ROMAN DRESSING COMBS

Perseus, addressing a young debauchee, asks why he takes such care of his head, while he bestows so much pain in removing the hair from every part of the body. There were also men who plucked beards, but this was a rare practice.

In the second century AD, the Roman man in rising gave much time to his toilet. He usually gave himself over to his tonsor, who arranged his hair in imitation of the emperor's style, which was initially simple and careless. However, after Hadrian's time, hair was crimped with curling irons even for those mature men. In general, the Romans were very attentive to their hair and beard. In fact, if a man's hair showed neglect and careless attention, he was likely to be treated with contemptuous scorn or open insult. Horace, the old Roman poet, described a man of high social finish as "politus ad ugnuem" —polished to the nail point.

Naturally, with all this interest in hair, the barber was kept busy practicing his trade. The barber, himself, furnished an excellent substitute for the modern newspaper. However, he was also a master at his art. The Roman barbers were said to have possessed great skill in removing grey hairs from the beard to enable middle-aged men to retain their youthful appearance. Galen, who became in time a famous Roman physician, described in some of his works various methods of freeing the chin of its hair growth, mentioning the ointments and oils used for this purpose. Many of the rich nobles had private tonsors, as they were then called. However, for the most part, the professional barber depended upon the poorer class for his steady trade.

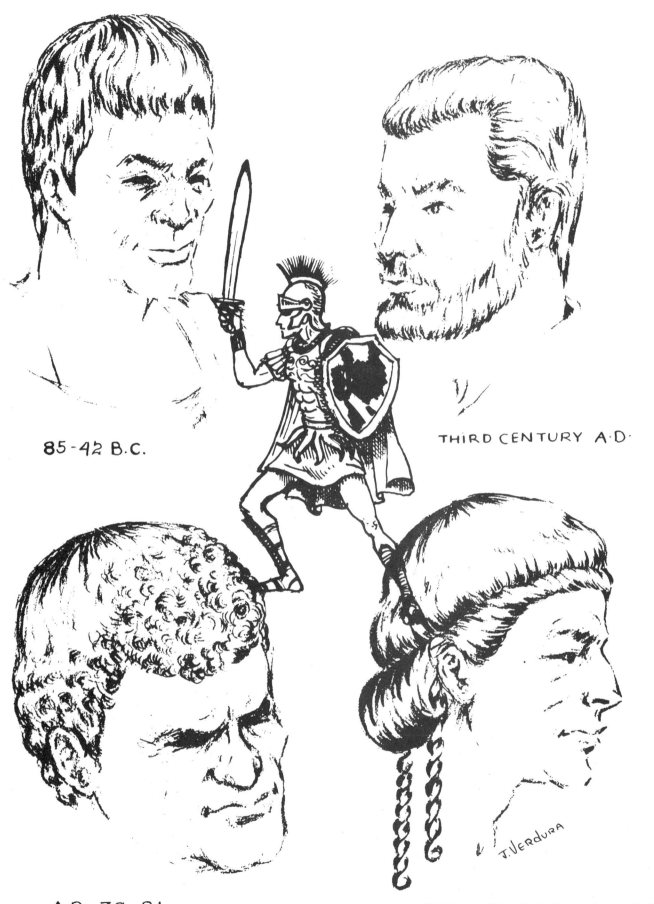

85-42 B.C.

THIRD CENTURY A·D·

A·D· 79-81

SECOND CENTURY A·D

SHORT, CURLED HAIR.

Generally speaking, Roman hairstyles were similar to those of the Greeks. For the most part, hair was worn relatively short and combed forward. Fashionable young men often curled or frizzed their hair, and until A. D. 268, sometimes wore gold dust, as did Nero. After the third century, it was usually brushed straight forward, although gentlemen of fashion curled it all over the head. The Romans were clean-shaven until the Second Century A.D., when beards came into favor. According to Roman custom, young men let their beards grow until they reached puberty, at which time it was consecrated to a god. When Nero dedicated his first beard, he encased it in a gold box, laden with pearls.

71

ABOVE: AN UNKNOWN ROMAN. Athens National Museum.

RIGHT: FULL, MODERN BEARD reflecting Roman influence. Hairstyle by Frank Leone. Photo: Kenn Duncan (Courtesy of Men's Hairstylist).

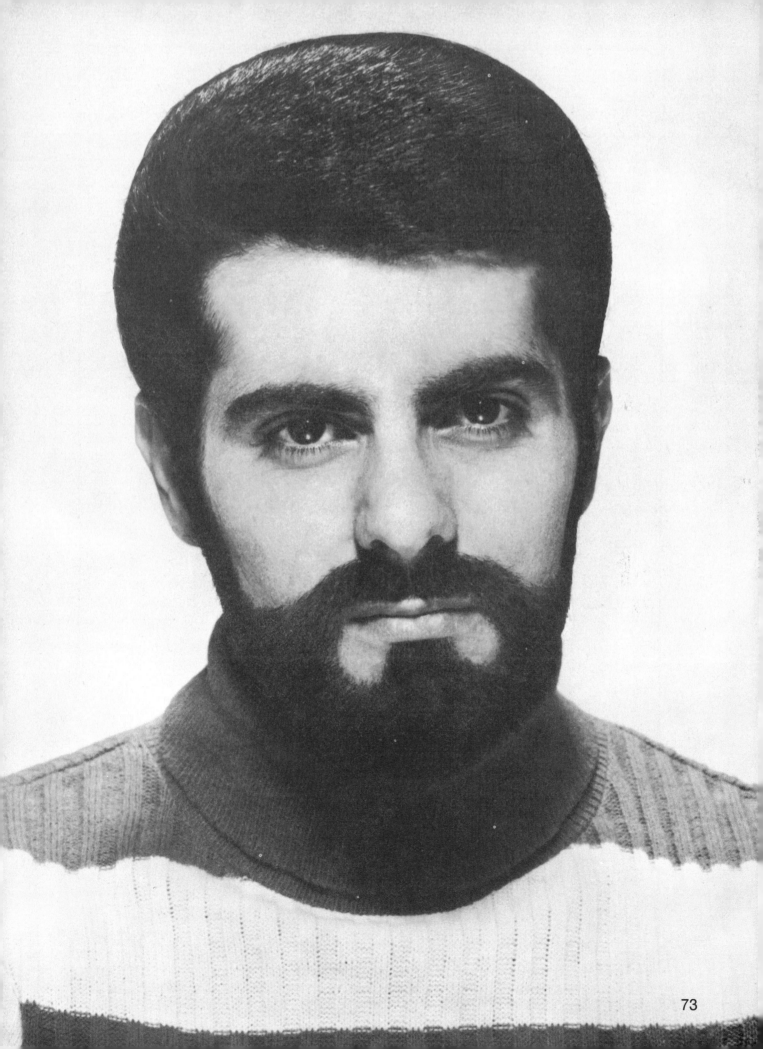

THE TONSURE refers to the shaven part of a priest's head. The ritual of shaving the crown of the head was referred to as the Tonsure of St. Peter. Shaving the whole head was referred to as the Tonsure of St. Paul.

CHAPTER V
THE MIDDLE AGES

Is There
A Doctor
In The House?

The Middle Ages was probably one of the most colorful periods in the history of barbering. It was the era of the barber-surgeons.

During the first centuries of the Christian era, the monks and priests were considered the most learned people of the times. As a result, they became the doctors of the Dark Ages, employing barbers as their assistants. However, during those days, the art of surgery was limited to blood-letting. When a person became ill, especially if he had a fever, it was immediately decided that he had too much blood in his system, and therefore, it was time for another blood-letting. To remove the excess blood, leeches or blood suckers were placed on the body to extract the necessary amount.

In 1163, the Council of Tours declared that it was sacrilegious for the clergy to practice blood-letting. Therefore, they relinquished their duties as physicians or surgeons. As a result, the barbers took over where the clergy left off, and the era of the barber-surgeons began.

DURING THE FIRST CENTURIES OF THE CHRISTIAN ERA, the monks and priests acted as doctors, with barbers as their assistants. Courtesy of Rockefeller Center, Inc.

BARBER'S BASIN, as used during the Middle Ages. Courtesy of Rockefeller Center, Inc.

In the years that followed, the town barber became the custodian of leeches and was called in whenever such an operation had to be performed. He kept the leeches in a basin and supplied the necessary bandages for protecting the wounds. Blood letting enjoyed such popularity, that it was customary to go for a blood letting every spring and fall. In fact, in order to get more of this lucrative business, many barbers engaged in price wars with their competitors. One barber outdid his competitors by putting up this sign: "Many boast of their low fee for blood letting, I give it free."

FRENCH BARBER DURING THE THIRTEENTH CENTURY

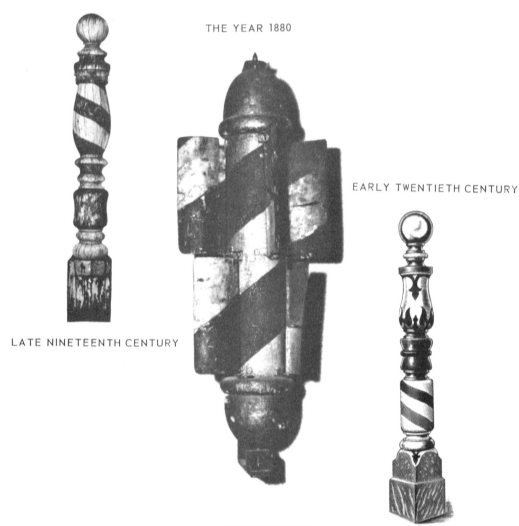

THE YEAR 1880

EARLY TWENTIETH CENTURY

LATE NINETEENTH CENTURY

BARBER POLES

The barber pole came into existence to indicate that a particular barber was also a leech doctor. The original pole had a brass basin at the top, representing the vessel in which the leeches were kept. The pole, itself, was the staff which the patient held onto during the operation. The red and white stripes represented the bandages, red for the bandage which would naturally be stained with blood during the operation, and white for a clean bandage. Originally, when not in use, the pole with a bandage wound around it, was hung at the door as a sign. But, later, for convenience, instead of hanging out the original pole, another one was painted in imitation of it and given a permanent place on the outside of the shop. The modern barber pole differs from the original barber pole in the respect that it has a ball instead of a basin at the top, and it has red, white, and blue stripes. The original barber pole had no blue stripe.

THE BATTLE BETWEEN THE BEARDED AND THE BEARDLESS existed throughout the Middle Ages. The monks pictured here evidently favored the latter trend. Courtesy of Rockefeller Center, Inc.

RICHARD LE BARBOUR
rebuking an ill-behaved barber, 1308

In the middle of the 13th century, the barber companies of Paris, known as the Brotherhoods of St. Cosmos and St. Damain, founded the first school ever known for the systematic instruction of barbers in the practice of surgery. The school was later enlarged and became the model school of surgery during the Middle Ages. In 1308, the first barber organization known as the Worshipful Company of Barbers was established. Richard le Barbour, master of the barbers, would make the rounds each month and rebuke any barbers whom he found acting disgracefully or entering another trade less reputable. In an order issued by le Barbour, barbers were forbidden to display vessels of blood in their windows . . . the blood was to be unobtrusively taken out and deposited in the Thames, the common sewer of London. Any barber found disobeying le Barbour's rules, would pay for it at the city jail. It wasn't until 1745, that the alliance between the barbers and surgeons was completely dissolved. This put an end to the old nursery rhyme, "O Mamma! What A Pain I've Got! I Must Be Off To The Barber Shop."

MEDIUM-LENGTH HAIR, as worn by Louis III. Ninth Century

SHOULDER LENGTH HAIR AND BEARD, as worn by Louis VII

The Middle Ages marked an era of beards, bowl cuts, and free-flowing tresses. During the 9th and 10th centuries, men wore their hair on the short side, in keeping with the Roman conquerors. However, some hairstyles were of medium length, and occasionally, some were even shoulder length. The hair was usually combed out from the crown in different directions. Only the nobility and the dignitaries were allowed to wear long beards.

By the 11th century, the clergy tried to banish beards. However, beards and long hair were revived later in the century, curled, crimped, and plaited.

During the 12th century, shoulder length hair was the fashion favorite. A great deal of care was taken to crisp the ends with curling irons. Kings often wore "tails" hanging over one shoulder, and twisted their hair into tight curls. Beards were often dressed into two points, or interlaced with gold thread. In addition, they were covered with ointments, and encased in special beard bags overnight. It was also during the 12th century, that the fashion of flowing tresses came into being. This fashion became so popular that it lasted for three centuries.

In addition, the church also opposed artificial hair, with its fascinating power to disguise. The idea that some Christian might be wearing a wig made from the hair of an infidel even then burning in hell, haunted the clergy. They pointed out that Hannibal, the wicked pagan, displayed earthly vanity by his habitual use of two wigs, one for beautification and the other for military use.

48

Philippe, le long frere
de Loys. hutin fut le
XLVIII. ROY. de france
Regnav. ans trespassa
.1321.

Filippo Lungo, frllo di Ludouico Vtino, Quadragesimoottauo Redi Frácia, essédo morto il frllo senza
figliuoli maschy, fu da i Baroni eleto Redl 1316. Voleua il duca di Borgogna, ch il Regno fosse d'una fi
gliuola dell Vtino; ma pducedo oli altri Baroni la legge salica, qual nó uuole, ch'le donne succedino nella
Corona di Frácia, il duca s'ácquieto Tenne Filippo il Regno cinq, anni; accordò le cose della Fiá
dra pacificaméte, cosi ricercáto dal papa copiaceza al quale mádo anche un'exercito í jtalia in sauore
dri Genouesi, pati al suo tepo la Frácia una pessileza horribile, caggionata (pquáto si dise) dall'
empieta de Giudei, che ne furono aspraméte puniti.

The 13th century was a time of short, puffed out hairstyles. Short beards, as well as moustaches, covered the most fashionable faces. Men still resorted to crisping irons to curl their hair. Some hairstyles featured tight rolls on the forehead and along the nape of the neck. The centre parting and fringed effects were also popular. The Bohemian chronicle of Hagecius ab Hagek complained in 1329 that, "Men are beginning to wear long beards or bristling, barbaric-looking moustaches, just like cats and dogs."

The 14th century brought with it the return to long hair and beards. The style, first popular with the nobility, gradually spread to the entire populace. Edward XX was especially proud of his carefully curled moustache and provocative beard. The French beards, which tended to be shorter than the English, were met with great opposition by the Church. The Church in France prohibited the wearing of beards among the clergy.

Younger men favored hair that was rolled or tucked under close about the head. The hair was sometimes cut square across the forehead and brushed back at the ears in curls. In addition, there were those who wore long, flowing tresses.

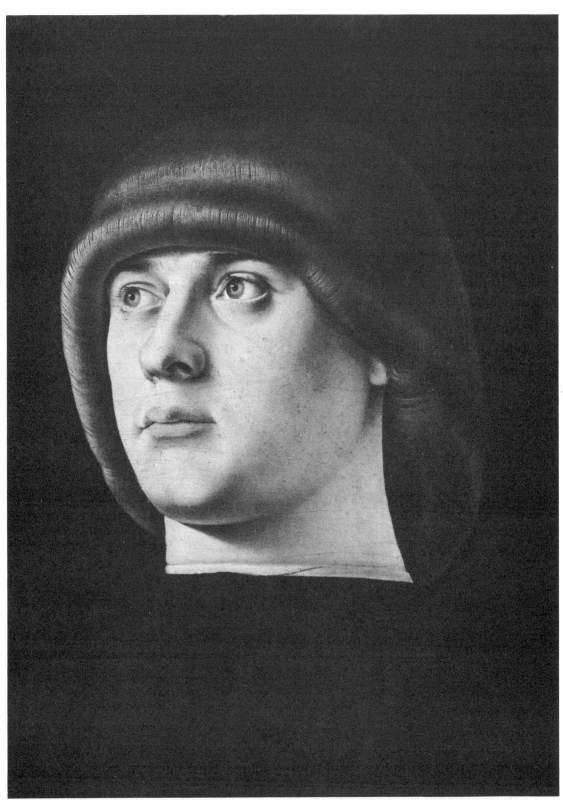

MEDIUM-LENGTH HAIR, as seen in Portrait of a Young Man. Oil painting by Giovanni Bellini.
Fifteenth Century. The Metropolitan Museum of Art.

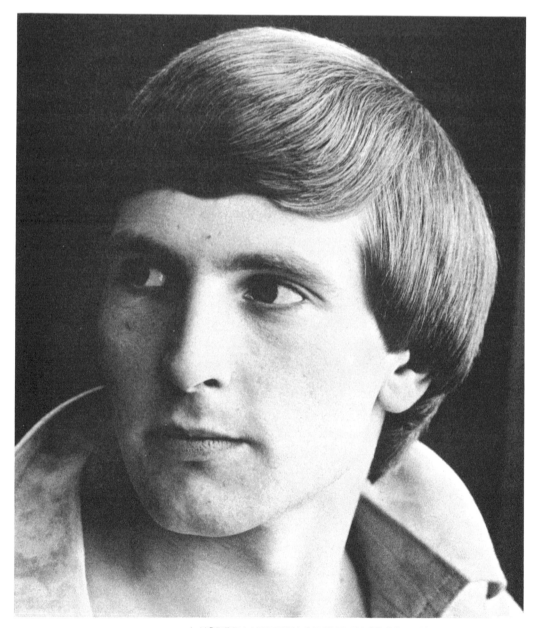

A MODERN VERSION OF THE PAGE-BOY. Photo: Kenn Duncan.

By the 15th century, hair was being worn in every conceivable shape and color. Sometimes it was straight, sometimes it was curled, and sometimes it was frizzed. If straight, the ends were usually turned under. If frizzed, the hair was usually of shoulder length and fluffy. It looked as though the hair had been tightly braided into tiny plaits at night, and then combed out in the morning. One of the most popular styles was the Florentine Cut, a shoulder length hairstyle that was frizzed all over.

One of the oddities of the century was the Bowl Crop (1410-1460), which was eventually adopted almost universally. This haircut resembled an inverted bowl with the rim reaching the top of the ears. The Modified Bowl Crop had longer hair covering the forehead, ears, and neck. The Page Boy Cut, which featured a center part of forehead fringe, was even as long as the shoulders.

15TH CENTURY
GERMAN

1412

15TH CENTURY ITALIAN

1448

John Verdura

LONG HAIR, as seen in the Portrait Of A Member Of The Este Family by Cosimo Tura.

The Metropolitan Museum of Art.

By the middle of the century, there were many longer, carefully curled hairstyles. The hair was put in curl papers and crimped. Young men often tied it up with ribbons. To keep their locks in place, men puffed out their hair with the aid of resin and the white of an egg. During the later years, some hairstyles reached to the shoulder and below. Long bangs were also in favor. Although beards were not very fashionable during this century, they were occasionally seen on older men, either rounded, pointed, or forked. In 1470, The Duke of Lorraine showed up wearing a false gold beard reaching down to his waist.

BLOND HAIR, as seen in Portrait of a Young Man. Oil painting by Antonello da Messina. The Metropolitan Museum of Art.

It was during the 15th century, that gentlemen either bleached their hair or wore wigs of blond or yellow silk. If their hair grew thin, they intertwined it with a yellow silk or gold thread. In addition, horse hair was used in the making of some wigs.

Black and blond were the two most desired hair colors during this era. Red hair was considered a curse. However, to really be in fashion, one had to be fair-haired. Both men and women colored their hair with a saffron, or an infusion of onion skin. It was Guillaume Coquillard who reveals this secret in his description of the young men of the Champagne country: "What would you say of our minion, who have brown hair, and who, of crushed skins of onions, make a vulgar juice, to turn it yellow." Dyes were also used to give instant youth. Mynon, an old man with white hair, when refused by a beautiful woman, dyed his hair black. He supposedly used worth flowers, a herb made popular by the Romans.

CHAPTER VI
THE SIXTEENTH CENTURY

To Beard
Or Not
To Beard

At the beginning of the century, shoulder length hair was still en vogue. The well-dressed man who was short on hair and long on fashion, turned to the wonders of the wig. Wigs of white or yellow silk, as well as those attached to tilted berets, were considered high fashion.

During this era, it was also fashionable to blacken the eyebrows, as noted in *Shadwell's Humourists.* "Be sure if your eyebrows are not black, to black 'em soundly. Ah! Your black eyebrow is your fashionable eyebrow. I hate rouges that wear eyebrows that are out of fashion."

Face-painting, as well as eyebrow plucking, was also favored. Henry III of France dusted his hair with a musk-scented powder, and wore a facial mask at night to soften his skin. Lead combs were used to restore color to faded hair. In addition, earrings, as well as civet and musk scents, were in general use.

The Elizabethan gentleman was extremely hair conscious. His increased wealth, and extravagant clothes, naturally demanded an elaborate hairstyle. The gallants of this era selected their gloves and perfumes with the greatest of care, and they often wore a single rose under their caps.

LEFT: BROAD BEARD AND MOUSTACHE, as seen in painting of Dirk Berck of Cologne by Hans Holbein (1497-1543). The Metropolitan Museum of Art.

16TH CENTURY
ITALIAN

16TH CENTURY
GERMAN

16TH CENTURY
FLEMISH

16TH CENTURY
SPANISH

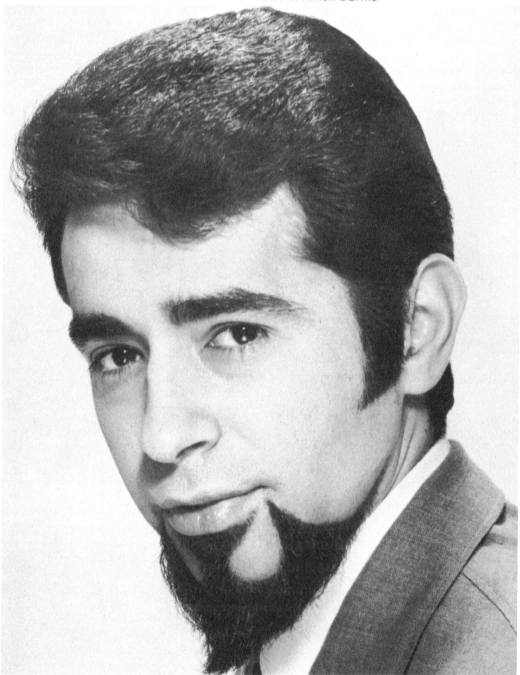

Photo: Kenn Duncan

Beards, varying in shape and size, were worn until the middle of the 16th century. The extremely long beards demanded very little care other than washing and combing. However, the short, fancy beards called for a hairdresser's attention. The Elizabethan barber stiffened, starched, powdered, perfumed, waxed, and even dyed his client's beard a fashionable red. Beards were curled with curling irons, and then shaped into a variety of styles. A man's beard could be cut pointed, square, round, oblong, or T-shaped. During the day, a beard brush was used to tidy up the beard, whereas during the night, it was a common practice to encase your beard in a special wooden press.

G. Talbot Earle of Shrewsbury

A FASHIONABLE GENT OF THE SIXTEENTH CENTURY.

The Elizabethan gallant often spent the entire day at the barber shop. Here's where he would smoke his tobacco, scribble a few verses, and exchange the gossip of the day. Generally speaking, the shop was more or less a club, where one could listen to the sounds of fiddles and flutes, as he awaited his turn. Musical instruments such as the violin, the lute, and the cittern, were also left around the shop for the entertainment of the customers.

However, in order to keep things under control, the owner would fine any customer who was handling razors or talking about throat cutting. One Elizabethan shop owner hung up this sign:

1) First come. First served.

2) Boots and spurs if worn are not to be used to hurt anyone.

3) Cursing and swearing to be fined seven farthings.

4) Fine of 1 pint of ale for interrupting the barber's discourse.

5) Fine of 1 pint of ale for losing the hat.

6) If the customer be unable to pay the barber's fee, he shall be sent away half-trimmed.

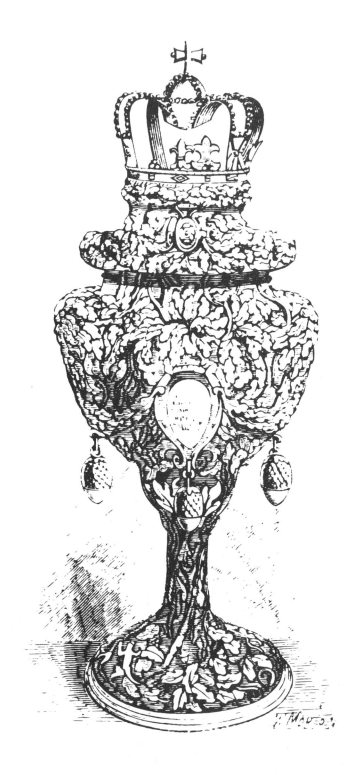

A VALUABLE GIFT, as presented to the barber-surgeons by royalty

KING HENRY VIII AND THE BARBER SURGEONS. From a painting by Hans Holbein.

Throughout the 16th century, barbers continued to let blood, pull teeth, and give haircuts. In 1540, the Guild of Surgeons was incorporated with the Barber's Company by act of parliament. The board of governors regulating this union consisted of two surgeons and two barbers. Every time a surgeon was granted a diploma entitling him to practice his profession, the diploma had to be signed by two barbers, as well as two surgeons. The surgeons resented this, but the barbers were very much favored by the monarchs, and preserved their privileges until the middle of the eighteenth century. Henry VIII, Charles II, and Queen Ann presented the barber-surgeons with valuable gifts and raised many of them to high offices. Under a clause in the Act of Henry VIII, the barber-surgeons were entitled to receive every year the bodies of four criminals who had been executed. The dissections were performed four times a year in the Barber Surgeon's Hall, which still stands in London.

In the later years, the Spanish fashion of pointed beards and waxed moustaches took over. The style of hairdressing varied from the short, curly coif of the '80s to the wearing of lovelocks in the '90s. Frenchmen curled their hair at the temples, often dressing it over wire frames.

Stubbs, in his *Anatomie of Abueses*, 1583, said: "They (the barbers) have invented such strange fashions of monstrous manners of cuttings, trimmings, shavings, and washings that you would wonder to see. They have one manner of cut called the French cut, another the Spanish; one the Dutch cut, another the Italian; one the new cut; another the old; one the gentleman's cut, another the common cut; one cut of the court, another of the country; with infinite like vanities, which I over-pass. They also have other kinds of cuts innumerable; and wherefore when you come to be trimmed they will ask you whether you will be cut to look terrible to your enemy or amiable to your friend; grim and stern in countenance, or pleasant and demure; for they have diverse kinds of cuts for all these purposes or else they lie. Then when they have done all their feats, it is a world to consider how their mustaches must be preserved or laid out, from one cheek to the other; or turned up like two horns towards the forehead."

By 1597, long hair was getting even longer. Consequently, this marked the beginning of over 200 years of lengthy locks, whether real or false.

LEFT: BEARD STYLES OF THE SIXTEENTH CENTURY: Left to Right, Top Line: Fool's Beard, Broad Spread-Out Beard, Swallow's Tail; Second Line: Tile Beard, Circular or Round Beard, Stubble Beard; Third Line: Long, Spread-Out Beard, Chin Tuft (Barbula or Pick-A-Devant), Stiletto or Bodkin and Pisa Beard.

CHAPTER VII
THE SEVENTEENTH CENTURY

Bewigged, Bothered, And Bewildered

During the 17th century, a well-dressed man kept his beard trimmed, his hands manicured, and his hair perfectly arranged. He took a fancy to earrings, patches, and sometimes, even paints.

In 1644, a work entitled, *Les lois de la galantrie francaise*, gave the following advice on the toilet: "Visit the baths occasionally to have a clean body. Everyday take the trouble to wash the hands and face as often as possible, and to shave the cheeks. Secure the services of a hairdresser."

Perfume was used not only because it was fashionable, but because it covered up tell-tale tobacco breath. *Le Parfumeur Francoys*, published in 1680, reveals, "His Majesty was often pleased to see Mr. Martial compose in his closet, the odors which he wore on his sacred person."

George Wilson, the herbalist, saw to it that his Majesty always had a generous supply of face lotion, honey water made from lemon rind, coriander, vanilla pods, cloves, nutmeg, storax, benzoin gum, and, of course, honey. A gentleman's dentifrice was supposedly made from bricks.

LEFT: LONG HAIR, and oddly-shaped moustache, as worn by the Earle of Clarendon, 1667.

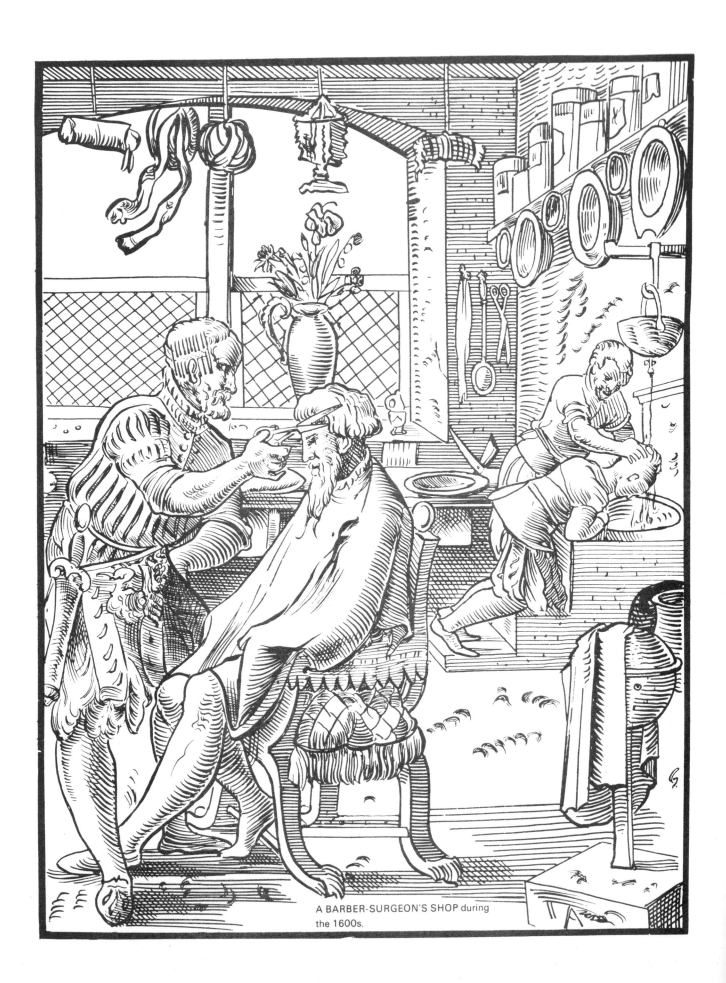

A BARBER-SURGEON'S SHOP during the 1600s.

The Barbers Shop. LXXV.   *Tonſtrina.*

The Barber, 1.	*Tonſor*, 1.
in the Barbers-ſhop, 2.	in *Tonſtrina*, 2.
cutteth off the Hair	tondet *Crines*
and the Beard	& *Barbam*
with a pair of Sizzars, 3.	*Forcipe*, 3.
or ſhaveth with a Razor,	vel radit *Novacula*,
which he taketh out of his	quam è *Theca*, 4. depromit.
Caſe, 4.	
And he waſheth one	Et lavat
over a Baſon, 5.	ſuper *Pelvim*, 5.
with Suds *running*	*Lixivio* defluente
out of a Laver, 6.	è *Gutturnio*, 6.
and alſo with Sope, 7.	ut & *Sapone*, 7.
and wipeth him	& tergit
with a Towel, 8.	*Linteo*, 8.
combeth him with a Comb, 9.	pectit *Pectine*, 9.
and curleth him	criſpat
with a Criſping Iron, 10.	*Calamiſtro*, 10.
Sometimes he cutteth a Vein	Interdum Venam ſecat
with a Pen-knife, 11.	*Scalpello*, 11.
where the Blood ſpirteth out,12.	ubi Sanguis propullulat, 12.
	The

A Page showing the Method of Teaching in the *Visible World*

Randall Holme in his *Heraldy* gives a vivid description of a 17th century barber shop:

"Inside, it contained an instrument case which held most of his tools. Among these tools was a looking-glass, a set of horn combs, for the combing and readying of long, thick and stony heads of hair and such like perriwigs, a set of ivory combs with fine teeth on both sides, an ivory beard-comb; a beard-iron called the forcepts for curling the beards; a set of razors; tweezers with an earpick; a rasp to file the point of a tooth; a hone for his razors; a bottle of sweet oil for his hone; a powder box with sweet powder; a puff to powder the hair; a four-square bottle with a screwed head and sweet water, wash balls and sweet balls; soap caps for the head to keep the hair up; trimming clothes to put before the man and napkins for his neck."

"After the client was shaved and bobbed," says Holme, "the barber was to hold him the glass, that he might see his newmade face. The barber was then to take off the linens, brush his clothes, present him with his hat, and make a low bow with your humble servant, sir."

Besides the books and musical instruments which were left around the shop, there was a spirit of gayiety which created a most pleasant atmosphere.

17TH CENTURY FRENCH

John Verdura

As the move towards longer hair started to gain hold, beards began to disappear. Some older men still kept their long beards; whereas the younger men turned to shorter beards and smaller moustaches. Beards were generally worn by older professional men. However, regardless of their size, great care was exercised in the care of the beard. The beard was kept in place by means of a small beard brush and comb, and a perfumed wax. In addition, if dyeing became necessary, the barber-surgeon was quick to assist his client in the coloring of same. A moustache band, of Spanish origin, was used to preserve the shape of the moustache, and a beard box protected a man's bristles during the night.

LOUIS XIII WEARING SHOULDER-LENGTH HAIR AND UPTURNED MOUSTACHE.

SEVENTEENTH CENTURY

HAIRSTYLES

During the early part of the century, the fashion of wearing wigs started to creep into the fashion scene. In 1624, Louis XIII, who was losing his hair, started to wear a wig. In those days, if a king wore a wig, so did the rest of the populace. The year 1660 is acknowledged as the year of the wig. However, the fashion did not catch on in England, until the reign of Charles II. Charles II began to wear a wig when his black hair started to turn grey. Once again, when the king had black hair, so did the rest of the populace. Later on, brown hair, as well as blond hair, became fashionable. Besides human hair, horsehair and goat's hair were used for gentlemen's wigs.

The early years reflected no great change in hairstyles and fashions. However, there was a great similarity in styles between the two sexes. If a man's hairstyle lengthened, chances are, his female counterpart would follow the same trend.

CLAVDIO RIDOLFI

Pittore di Figure, nacque in Verona
l'anno 1500. morì l'anno 1644.

Gio Dom Campiglia del.

Silv. Pomarede fc

SHOULDER LENGTH HAIR, as worn by Charles I of England. Note the earring and fancy beard and moustache.

At the beginning of James I's reign, men wore their hair relatively short. Eventually, it lengthened and was brushed back straight away from the face, and was worn without a part. Very often, the hair was slightly waved.

By the 1620s, men started to let their hair grow, with one or two ringlets falling onto the collar. Men with long, flowing tresses wore their hair parted in back and over the shoulders.

By the 1630s, there was a trend towards more frontal fringe. The fringe was often brushed to one side. If a gentleman had sparse hair around the temples, pieces of false hair, or "corners," as they were called, were added.

In 1636, Harvard College declared, "Nor shall it be permitted to wear long hairs, locks, foretops, curlings, crispings, partings, or powdering of ye haire."

The fashion of the lovelock—a curled lock of hair brought forward in front and tied with a ribbon—started to catch on towards the end of Elizabeth I's reign. This trend lasted until about 1680. For diversion, a bow or rosette was attached to the ends.

CHARLES THE II WEARING A LONG, CAREFULLY CURLED WIG.

Louis XIV didn't start wearing a wig until he was 35 years old. But when he acquired the custom, he had a wig for every occasion—one for getting up, another for going to sleep, one for church, one for after dinner, one for supper, etc. The king's personal barber, Binette, who shaved and trimmed his Majesty, was the only person who was ever allowed to see the king without his wig. However, at night, the wig was, supposedly, passed out between the drawn bed curtains, and the reverse procedure was performed in the morning.

In the last quarter of the century, wig-making became an important art. French wigs, in particular, were in demand all over Europe. In the earlier wigs, hair was sewn to a calotte of silk. However, now the strands were drawn through canvas and held by individual knots.

LEFT: LOUIS XIV POPULARIZED THE ENORMOUS PERIWIG.

EARLY WIGS, a cascade of free-flowing curls.

The fashion in wigs varied from year to year. The early wigs were a cascade of free-flowing curls which tumbled around the shoulders. The newer wigs were smaller and less pretentious, and resembled natural hair. Then the periwigs came into fashion. They were very large wigs, with regular curls. Louis XIV, with his enormous periwig parted in the center, popularized this fashion. Even a set of riglets or a single curl was considered a wig. In addition, the full-bottomed wig which appeared in the second half of the 17th century, was worn over a shaved head. What started out as a substitute for thinning hair, developed into an artificial-looking head of hair. In 1678, LeMercure Galant described two wigs, half frizzed and half curled, and made mention of cavalier wigs with a large curl.

In the midst of all this wig-wearing, the hair was still scented and sometimes dyed. Powder made of morris and nutmeg was also worn on the hair.

CHAPTER VIII
THE EIGHTEENTH CENTURY

Macaroni Madness

In 1754, the editors of *Connoisseur* described the dandy of the day: "The male beauty has his washes, perfumes, and cosmetics, and takes as much pains to set a gloss on his complexion as the footman in japanning his shoes. He will spend his whole morning scenting his linen, dressing his hair, and arching his eyebrows. His head, as well as the lady's, has undergone various mutations and has worn as many different kinds of wigs as the block at his barber's. About fifty years ago, the fashionable man buried his head in a bunch of hair; and the beaux, as Swift says, 'lay hid beneath the penthouse of a full-bottomed perriwig.' But as they showed nothing but the nose, mouth, and eyes, the fine gentlemen of our time not only oblige us with their full faces, but have drawn back the side curls quite to the top of the ear."

Upon describing a young man's dressing room, the editors went on to say: "I could not help but observe a number of boxes in different sizes—all from Japan. They lay regularly disposed on the table. I had the curiosity to examine the contents of several: In one I found lip-salve, in another a roll of pig-tail, and in another, the ladies black sticking plaster; but the last which I opened, very much surprised me, as I saw nothing in it but a number of little pills. I likewise remarked, on one part

LEFT: DANDY'S TOILETTE

Morning . . . Noon . . . Night.

The HEN-PECKED DANDY.

GEORGE WASHINGTON. Painting by Gilbert Stuart, 1803.

of the table, a tooth-brush and sponge, with a pot of Delescot's opiate; and a roll of perfumed pomatum. Almond pastes, powder puffs, hair combs, brushes, nipper, and the like, made up the rest of this fantastic equipage. But among many other whimsies, I could not conceive for what use a very small ivory comb could be designed, till the valet informed me it was a comb for the eyebrows."

In addition, face patches were used in the same way that political buttons are used today. Patching the face, which was originally designed to camouflage facial blemishes, became a popular fashion during the days of the dandy.

The American Colonist, according to one source, would also use patches or mouches, as the finishing touch to his good grooming ritual. This ritual made use of scissors, curling irons, razors, lotions, perfumes, powders, and paints. The first step involved lathering and shaving the face. Lotion was used for this purpose, as water was not considered an effective cleansing agent. After cleansing, a rouge was applied over the foundation. A fine powder was then dusted onto the skin to tone down any harsh colorings. As an optional step, patches—small bits of gummed silk in various shapes and designs, were applied. The American Colonist, as did our own George Washington, enjoyed the fragrance of sweet-smelling scents. Frenchmen reportedly favored Eau de Cologne, whereas Englishmen preferred lavender water.

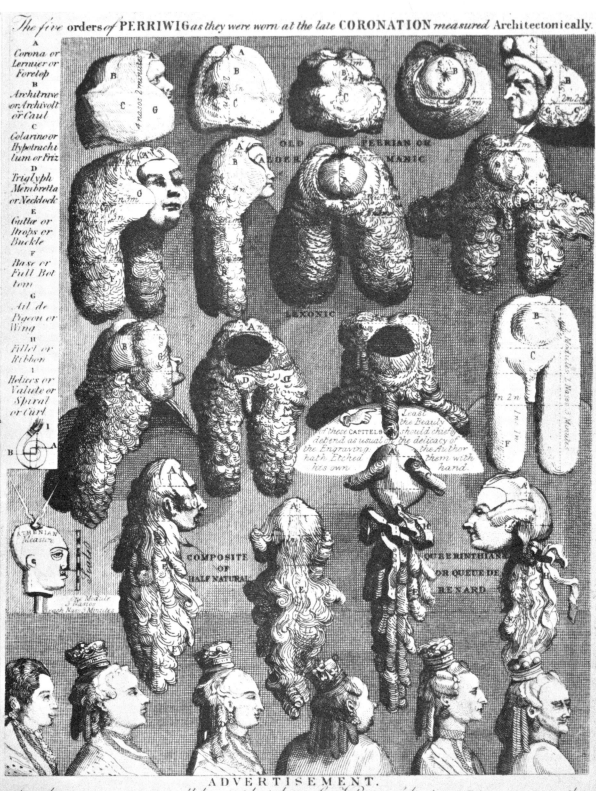

The five orders of PERRIWIG as they were worn at the late CORONATION measured Architectonically.

During the 18th century, it was not unusual for a man of fashion to spend hours in the arrangement of his hair. In the morning, he usually visited his barber, and during the evening, his barber usually visited him. These elaborate hairstyles took several hours to complete, and generally lasted two to three weeks before being redone. Prince Belgiojoso of Milan had a barber who came once a month from Paris to dress his hair in the latest fashion.

What the wigs of the 18th century lacked in bulk, they more than made up for in variety. Once a new style was introduced, it was added to the others that were already in fashion, and eventually, the variety of wigs just grew and grew. Never before had men such a wide selection from which to choose. A man could change his style as often as his pocketbook could afford. As the wig decreased in price, the middle classes adopted the trend. Eventually, even the poorer classes could afford a wig. And those that couldn't, would often dress their hair to look like a wig.

With hair being of such great importance, the art of combing came into vogue. Combing one's hair in public was a popular pastime. The theater, in particular, was considered an especially good place to exhibit the art. According to one source, you could spot a country novice, by "his habit of combing his wig with his fingers." Large pocket combs, in ivory, silver, and tortoise shell, were carried along with snuff boxes.

The better wigs utilized only human hair. The hair from the northern countries was supposedly the best. Stewart in his writings reveals, "The merit of good hair consists of its being well fed and neither too coarse, nor too slender, the bigness rendering it less susceptible of the artificial curl and disposing it rather to frizzle, and the smallness making its curl of too short duration."

Besides human hair, the cheaper wigs used horse hair and goat's hair. In addition, feathers were often substituted for real hair. A special "feather-top" wig was worn by sportsmen and parsons. One peruke maker advertised, "Very durable wigs, not to be hurt at least by wet, made of the single feathers in mallard tails." Another ad dated 1761 offered, "Gentlemen's perukes for sporting made of drakes' tails."

LA TOILETTE. Gentlemen holding a face cone, while being powdered. After Carle Vernet.

The Monthly Magazine of the 1800s gives a colorful description of an English statesman by saying, "He was one of the most fashionable figures about town wearing his red heeled shoes and blue hair powder." Indeed, a well-dressed gentleman spent a great deal of time in seeing to it that his hair was properly powdered. It was so important a function, that special powder closets were designed specifically for this purpose. Those who could not afford powder closets, sent their wigs to the local wig-maker. However, many depended upon the services of a skilled valet.

The technique of powdering the hair was a messy process. The powder was blown onto the hair with special bellows. To prevent the client from being entirely covered with flour, a face mask and apron offered the necessary protection. Sometimes the powder was blown directly towards the hair, or it was often blown towards the ceiling, and then allowed to float downward.

Prior to powdering, the hair was coated with grease or pomatum. This supposedly kept the powder in place. However, not all the powder stayed where it was supposed to. As Gay so aptly cautions us, "On meeting a coxcomb, pass with caution by, lest from his shoulders clouds of powder fly."

Wheat flour was the first substance used for powdering. Pure white powder was introduced in 1703. It was estimated that in the time of George II, the average soldier used about a pound of flour a week on his hair. Powders were also made from earth and a mixture of starch and plaster of paris. Although the average man favored white and grey powder, the dandies went in for a variety of colors, namely, brown, black, blond, pink, blue, and lavender—all heavily scented, of course. The fashion of powdered wigs lasted for almost 100 years, only coming to a close with the end of the French Revolution.

Wigs were considered just as good as natural hair, and no man ever thought of concealing the fact that he wore a wig. On the contrary, to wear a wig was to be in fashion. In 1763, the Master Peruke Makers of London petitioned the king to pass a law which would oblige every man to wear a wig.

The FEMALE SHAVER

Pub.ᵈ Jan.ʸ 1.1773. by MDarly 39 Strand.

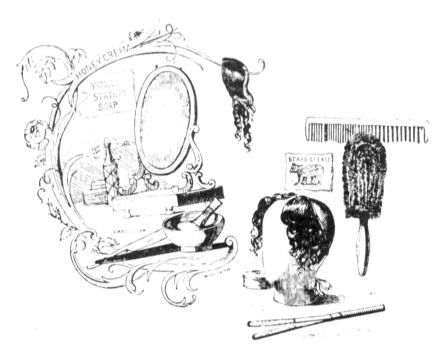

Special pipes were used to curl the wigs. According to Redfern, "These were of pipe-clay and were heated over a stove, and when the pipes were sufficiently hot they were used on the wigs in the same way as curling tongs are now employed. The various sizes range from the small pipe for the upper part of the wig to the enormous roulette which formed the larger curls at the lower end of it."

James Stewart, in his writings of 1783, points out that "It is certain, gentlemen's hair cannot be curled and dressed in perfection without putting it in papers." He suggests the following: "You are to proceed in every shape as you did when you curled the ladies' hair, only with this difference; you must make more curls, or papers, the hair being shorter, else it will not have a curl strong enough. Most gentlemen for four or five months in the year have their hair in a brush, within half an inch of their skull, which must naturally strengthen it much, and effectually counteract any bad consequences from the toupee irons. When, therefore, gentlemen's hair is turned, or toupeed, it is done in regular rows exactly as the ladies' has been directed. If the gentlemen wears a false tail, you are to shove it in the middle of the tail, when the hair covers it on all sides; you are then to press the hair exceedingly tight down with your hands, and in order that it may tie well, the gentlemen must fall his head between his shoulders."

Natural hair was curled by means of curl papers or papillottes. For frizzed effects, small tight curls were created, and then combed out into a bush.

EARLY 18TH CENTURY
GERMAN

MID-CENTURY
ENGLISH.

1735 ENGLISH

LATE 18TH CENTURY
POLISH SOLDIER

During the early years, the full-bottomed wig was still in fashion. These heavy, pretentious wigs were a cascade of curls. A center parting was usually seen, from which point the hair was dressed into two exaggerated peaks.

However, underneath this mass of curls, a shaved head prevailed. All men, except those of the lower classes, resorted to the razor. This, supposedly, kept the head clean, and guarded against the invasion of vermin. Even at bedtime, the head was never exposed. On the contrary, all men wore night caps of some kind, with some being more luxurious than others. The poorest men settled for unbleached homespun, whereas the richest men, insisted on luxury fabrics, laden with stones, A French manual on the *Art of Dress* warned against the anti-aphrodisiac effects of the night cap by saying, "Grand Dieu! What would a young and pretty woman say now if she would see, lying beside her, her husband, or what would be still worse, her lover tucked up in a well-starched cotton night cap—the poor woman would be paralyzed."

After 1730, there was a movement towards smaller, less pretentious wigs. The full-bottomed wig declined in popularity, although it was still worn by some elderly men and professional groups. It was during this period that the toupee came into fashion. Instead of having a center part, the hair was brushed away from the face into a Modified Pompadour. The front of the hair was usually brushed over the edges of the wig to conceal a less-than-perfect hairline. Sometimes, the wearer's natural hair was blended into the wig. The foretop of the natural hair or of the wig was known as a toupee. As the toupee gained in importance, it slowly worked its way to the crown . . . past the crown . . . and finally, across the entire head. By 1750, toupees were increasing in height, and by 1770, the Macaronies were wearing highly exaggerated toupees, which were built up on wire frames or felt cushions.

BOBS, BOB-MAJORS SCRATCHES & other wigs made here, also SAUSAGES, WASHBALLS Black Puddings Scotch Pills, Powder for the ITCH, REDHERRINGS, BREECHES BALLS & Small BEER by the maker —

BARN: FACTOTUM
Drefses Shaves
& Bleeds &c.
IN UTRUMQUE PARATUS.

THE TOWN BARBER.

THE FASHIONABLE QUEUE of the Eighteenth Century

Group from Hogarth's print of 'Taste in High Life.'

In the meantime, men grew tired of wearing so much hair on their faces, and started to tie it back as a means of comfort and convenience. With the hair tied back, the sides were left to hang loosely. This inspired men to wear as many as five roll curls at the sides, or one big roll curl which extended across the entire head.

After 1740, wigs with queues came into fashion. The queue was the hair which hung down the back of the head. Included in this category, was the tie-wig, which was simply tied back with a black ribbon, the Ramillies wig, which had either one or two plaits, and a large bow at the end of the plait, the bag wig, which had a draw-string bag in which the hair was encased, the pig-tail wig which was interlaced with black ribbon, and the Cadagon or club wig which had the hair looped into a broad, flat back.

In addition, wigs without queues continued throughout the century. During the early years, the knotted wig, an outgrowth of the full-bottomed wig, was tied at the ends. There were also bob wigs . . . short bobs to expose the neck, and long bobs of shoulder length. There was also the bushy campaign wig with center parting and bushy sides, and the scratch wig, which could be worn either dressed or disheveled.

CHIRURGYN
a La Mode

C. Troost pinxit.
P. Tanjé fecit.

ARLEQUIN
TOOVENAAR en BARBIER.

Zo! Meester Arlequin! gy kunt u kunstig weeren.
Straf deeze Snoevers vry voor hunn' vermeetlen waan.
Maar zo gy, in deeze Stad, moet all hun Makkers scheeren,
't Gaat vast, gy had uw werk in lang niet afgedaan.
L.P.

DEDIÉ a MONSIEUR ANTOINE
Conseiller actuël des Mines de sa
et son Commissaire tres merité pour

Tc Amsterdam by P. Fouquet Junior 1756.

ARLEQUIN
MAGICIEN & BARBIER.

Arlequin, feint Barbier, dans son art est habile.
Ces Fanfarons en font l'épreuve, à leurs depens;
Mais s'il devoit raser tous leurs pareils en Ville,
Comment suffiroit-il à servir ses Chalands?
H.J.R.

JOSEPH DE BERGK,
Majesté Imperiale & Royale;
la Chambre aulique des Finances;

Tiré du Cabinet de Mr. Abraham van Broyel
de la même grandeur que l'Original.

Par son tres humble Serviteur P. Fouquet Junior.

THE MILITARY WIG OF THE EIGHTEENTH CENTURY

As early as the '60s, there was evidence that men were going back to natural hair. Some men started wearing their natural hair, and others powdered their heads only upon special occasions. However, the *Encyclopedia Perruquiere* of 1764 was still describing 115 different styles of perukes. The "peruke" usually meant the more formal, elaborate wig. The "periwig" referred to wigs of a less formal nature.

The wigs were either dressed by a local wig-maker, or a special valet. The well-groomed man saw to it that his wig was always properly dressed, especially on weekends. Barber boys were often seen carrying their wig boxes from house to shop on Saturday afternoons.

Since beards were out, shaving was in. Barbers were kept busy gilding the razor, since few men knew how to shave themselves. Although the barbers, in general, kept their client's confidence, there were some nasty rumors about barbers being able to supply fresh corpses on split-second notice. In 1745, after a union of over 200 years, the era of the barber-surgeon was over. They were now separated into two distinct guilds, namely, barbers and surgeons.

THE COVENT GARDEN MACARONIES.

Pub by M Darly Strand Feby 24th 177[?]acor to act.

SENATORS
of New York in 1798

MR L. HOMMEDIEU   MR GOLD.   MR JONES.

MR CANTINE   MR SILVESTER   MR GRAHAM

As wigs gained in popularity, they became symbols of class distinction. In 1786, Jacques Dulaure, referring to the French fashions wrote: "Tradesman—to appear as he ought, should have his head shaved and wear a round wig; physicians and surgeons, too, should do the same. Who, in this enlightened age, would put the best confidence in a physician, who wears his own hair, were it the finest in the world. A wig, certainly, can't give him science, but it gives him the appearance, and that is everything nowadays."

James Stewart in his writings pointed out that, "As the peruke became more common, their shape and forms altered. Hence we hear of the clerical, the physician, and the tie peruke for the man of the law, the brigadier or major for the army and navy, as also the tremendous fox-ear or cluster of temple curls with a pig-tail behind. The merchant, the man of business and of letters, were distinguished by the grave full-bottom, or more moderate tie, neatly curled; the tradesman by the snug bob or natty scratch, the country gentleman by the natural fly and hunting peruke."

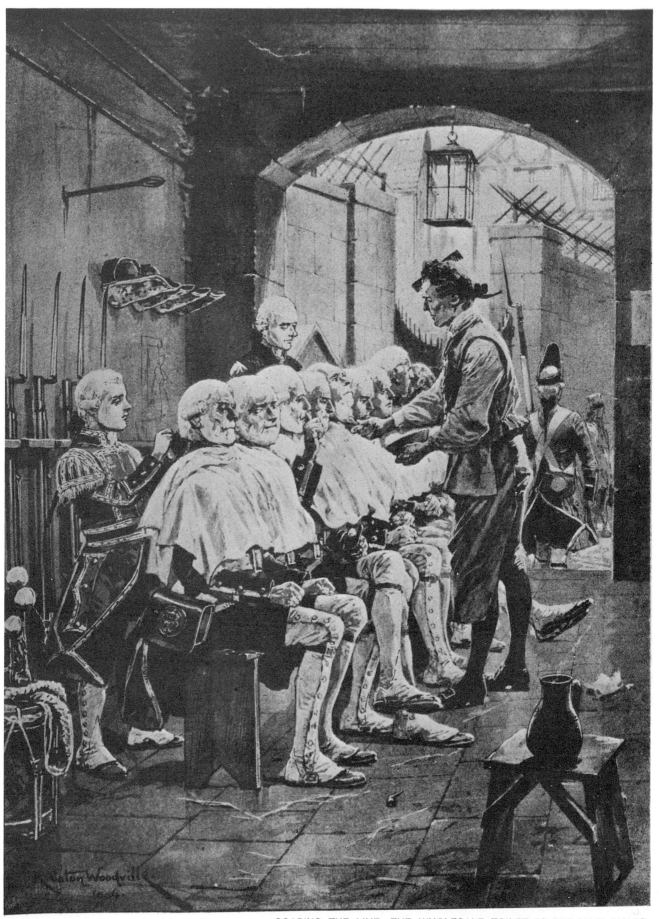

SOAPING THE LINE: THE WHOLESALE TOILET OF THE MAIN GUARD.

In the early years, wigs with queues were worn only by the military. The *Irish Quarterly Review* reported: "There was the thick braid of hair hanging down between the shoulders, the smaller tail, tightly bound up with black ribbon; the loosely tied tail, the tail of the courtier, with a bag attached to it; the short medical tail; the gentleman's tail, and military tails invented in the time of the Duke of York, which, looking like a small riding whip and hanging between the shoulders, was supposed to ward off the cut of a sabre; but which caused so much pain and inconvenience when fastened to the hair, that officers frequently attached theirs to their caps or helmets; and a row of tails might be seen hanging up in the hall, while their owners were at dinner, rejoicing in their freedom." Wigs with queues became fashionable about 1740.

The British Army kept special curl patterns on file, which the barber had to follow. On one occasion, it was reported that since there were not enough barbers to go around, the officers had to have their hair powdered and plastered the day before, and therefore, had to sleep face down all night in order not to disturb the elaborate coiffures. By 1790, not only was natural hair on its way back, but short hair was, too. Since the head was shaved for wig-wearing, it took some time for the hair to grow out into an acceptable style. In the interim, partial wigs were often used. However, once the natural hair was of the desired length, the wig was discarded.

Short haircuts were first introduced in France, and then the rest of the world. However, some older men and professional groups continued to wear their wigs well into the 19th century. In addition, some men although they favored the return to natural hair, kept their hair long and flowing. The so-called Brutus crop, was worn by both sexes, and looked almost disheveled.

CHAPTER IX
THE NINETEENTH CENTURY

The Moustache Movement

At the beginning of the 19th century, the wig was not only going, it was practically gone. Usually, only elderly men or the military were seen with their powdered wigs. The American soldier's queue was cut off entirely by 1808.

During the early years, styles were short and rather full in front. The styles were somewhat reminiscent of the Roman Empire. The ends were usually brushed over the forehead and onto the cheeks. By 1809, curly hair, worn in loose ringlets, started to make its way into men's fashion.

During this century, a gentlemen's toilet was to include the following:

1) A good sharp knife to cut the nails.
2) Tweezers to remove superfluous hair from face, neck, ears, and nose.
3) Hair oils (castor oil stiffened with bees wax and meal is best).
4) Hair dye for hair and beard.
5) Perfumed chalk if the complexion is inclined to be sallow.
6) A little rouge to be used carefully so as to avoid detection.

LEFT: SIDE WHISKERS, as worn during the 1820s.

EARLY 19ᵗʰ CENTURY
HAITIAN

1833 ENGLISH

1877 AMERICAN

John Verdura

CONFEDERATE SURGEON GENERAL

The 19th century witnessed the development of a variety of hair care products. Alexander Rowland introduced Rowland's Macassar Oil as early as 1793. It became so popular that society eventually invented an anti-macassar. Byron in his *Don Juan*, exclaimed, "In virtues nothing earthly could surpass her, save thine incomparable oil macassar." However, other authorities, such as the author of the *Art of Beauty* in 1825, had other viewpoints: "We are assured that this is advertised at the rate of some hundreds, if not thousands, annually. The public, of course, pay smartly for this, as well as for the cheap materials of which it is composed. The following we believe to be the genuine recipe for its preparation:

'Take three quarts of common oil, half a pint of spirits of wine, three ounces of cinnamon powder, two ounces of bergamot. Put it in a large piplin, and give it a good heat. When it is off the fire, add three to four pieces of alkonet root, and keep it closely covered for several hours. Filter it through a funnel lined with blotting paper. The commonest oil is used, and when rancid, it is remedied by putting in two or three slices of an onion. Not an ounce of Macassar oil is imported from Macassar, or it would be entered at the customs, which it is not.'

Moustache wax, of course, was very popular. The wax, which was a mixture of white bees wax and pomade, affixed the hairs into place.

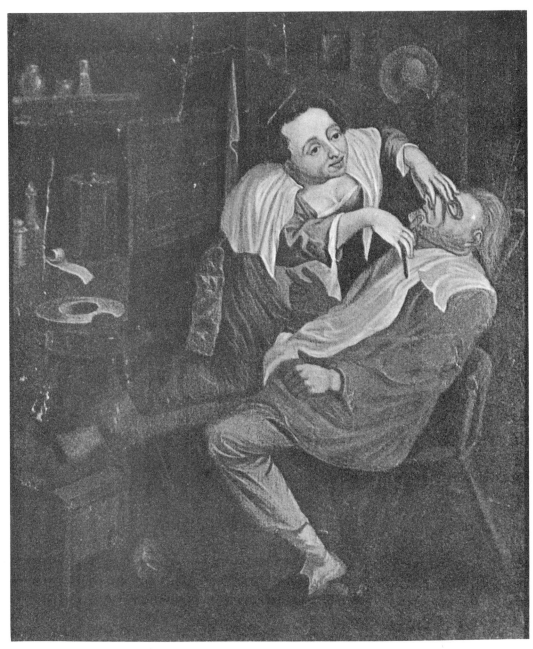

LADY BARBER GIVING A SHAVE. From the Charles DeZemler Collection. Courtesy of Rockefeller Center, Inc.

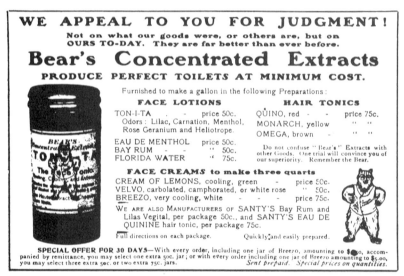

BEAR'S CONCENTRATED EXTRACTS, from an advertisement

Then there was always Spencer's Chinese liquid hair dye which, "Changed in a few minutes with the trouble red or grey hair whiskers, eyebrows, moustaches, etc. to dark brown or black by simply using a comb wetted with this liquid—a pleasing and permanent finish."

Anyone who was unable to grow back a new head of hair, could always use Cantharides Oil (Spanish Fly was the acting ingredient) and if that failed, there was always the much advertised, "gentlemen's real head of hair, or invisible ventilating peruke."

As for the popular bear's grease, one 19th century author described it as follows: "There are two sorts of it; one of the consistence of thick olive oil, which is procured by boiling from the fat about the caul and the intestines of the animal; the other, much harder, and in appearance, like frozen honey, obtained from the kidneys. Both sorts have a rank, rancid, and intolerable smell."

In *Master Humphrey's Clock*, Dickens introduced a barber who overspent on bears. An ad in the *Daily Universal Register* reported: "H. Little, Perfumer; No. 1 Portugal Street, Lincoln's Inn Fields, acquaints the public, that he has killed a remarkable fine Russian Bear, the fat of which is matured by time to a proper state. He begs leave to solicit their attention to this animal, which, for its fatness and size, is a real curiosity. He is now selling the fat, cut from the animal, in boxes—or rendered down in pots from one shilling to one guinea each. Mr. Little was a big enterpriser, however, unlike a certain rival in the trade, he did not caution his buyers "to keep the grease off the backs of their hands less they grow hairy paws."

FASHIONABLE GENT OF THE 1830s.

BEARDED LADY of the Nineteenth Century

As wigs continued to fall in disfavor, barbers started to sell more products to preserve the natural hair. In a book entitled, *The Whole Art of Dress, or the Road to Elegance and Fashion at the Enormous Saving of Thirty Per Cent* published in 1830, a Cavalry officer gives away his secret formula for hair oil:

"The following recipe for making an economical beautifier of the hair, I am indebted to a friend for, as I have had so long a tried proof of its virtue, I can with pleasure impart it to others. 'Of fine beef marrow, take 1.2 lb., of burnt brandy, two tablespoonsful, with the same quantity of the best flask oil. These should be mixed and allowed to simmer over the fire, when it should constantly be skimmed until it boils; when, after boiling a little time, the perfume bergamot, musk, lavender, or rose as preferred, should be added, when it should be potted and tied up.' "

Another 19th century preparation, bay rum, was a hair wash and hair dressing which supposedly stimulated hair growth. Beard producers, such as the juice of onions, guranteed to raise a strong, full beard on the chins of youths in their fifteenth year. Years later, it was reported, a dock worker at Bristol rubbed sliced onion on his bald scalp and upon being asked if the solution was successful, he replied: "Yes, I have gained a few hairs, but lost many friends."

EDWARDS'

HARLENE "FOR THE HAIR

THE GREAT
Hair Producer & Restorer

The Very Finest Dressing, Specially Prepared and Perfumed, Fragrant and Refreshing.

A LUXURY AND A NECESSITY TO EVERY MODERN TOILET.

"HARLENE"

PRODUCES LUXURIANT HAIR, PREVENTS IT FALLING OFF OR TURNING GREY.

Unequalled for Promoting
the Growth of the Beard
and Moustache.

THE WORLD-RENOWNED

REMEDY

FOR

BALDNESS.

For Curing Weak and Thin
Eyelashes; Preserving, Strengthening, and Rendering the Hair
beautifully soft;

For Removing Scurf, Dandruff, &c.; also for RESTORING GREY HAIR TO ITS NATURAL COLOUR,

IT IS WITHOUT A RIVAL.

Physicians and Analysts pronounce it to be devoid of any metallic or other injurious ingredients.

WHY NEGLECT YOUR CHILDREN'S HAIR?

Edwards' "Harlene" Preserves, Strengthens, and Invigorates It.

Prevents and Cures all species of Scurf, Keeps the Scalp Clean, and Allays all Irritation.

The Hon. MRS. THOMPSON'S TESTIMONY.

"Ackworth Moor Top, Pontefract.

"The Hon. Mrs. Thompson desires to testify to the value of 'Harlene' for strengthening and preserving the hair, and will be pleased to allow her testimony to be publicly used."

PROVED IT HERSELF.

"59, Elgin Crescent, Notting Hill.

"Dear Sir.—I am delighted to add my testimony to the wonderful efficacy of your hair tonic. I never could have credited the effects of 'Harlene' had I not myself proved them.—Yours truly, "KATHERINE RAMSEY."

1s., 2s. 6d., and (triple **2s. 6d.** size) **4s. 6d.** per Bottle, from Chemists, Hairdressers, and Perfumers all over the World; or sent direct on receipt of Postal Orders.

EDWARDS' "HARLENE" CO., 95, HIGH HOLBORN, LONDON, W.C.

HAIR PRODUCER & RESTORER, from an advertisement, 1896

MAJ. GEN. BUTLER.   MAJ. GEN. WOOL.   MAJ. GEN. A.E. BURNSIDE.

MAJ. GEN. HALLECK   GEN. T.W. SHERMAN.   MAJ. GEN. BUELL

As one of the periodicals of the day explained it: "The substances in most general use at the present day, and whose virtues are most highly extolled for the restoration and improvement of the hair are, 'bear's grease, beef marrow, olive oil, oil of almonds, both sweet and bitter, oil of nuts, of camomile, and of laurel, goose grease, fox grease, fresh butter, burnt butter, and bees burnt and pounded in oil or roses. Some use brandy or honey water to make the hair grow. The juices of cresses and of onions are recommended by the school of Salernum for the same purpose, and for some, the juice of the white onion is preferred to the other kinds. Much is also made of nettle juice, sage, southern wood, dell, and the ashes of moles and hedgehogs."

The following recipes appeared in a work published in Paris called, *Manuel Cosmetiques des Plantes:*

"To make hair grow and prevent it from falling—take the roots of young vines, the roots of hemp, and young cabbages, of each two handsful, dry, and then burn them—make afterwards a lye with the ashes; before the head is washed with this lye, it must be rubbed with honey; and continue both for three successive days."

PROF. BARBER'S

GOOSE-GREASE

PRODUCES AN INSTANTANEOUS

LUXURIANT MOUSTACHE

ON THE SMOOTHEST LIP.

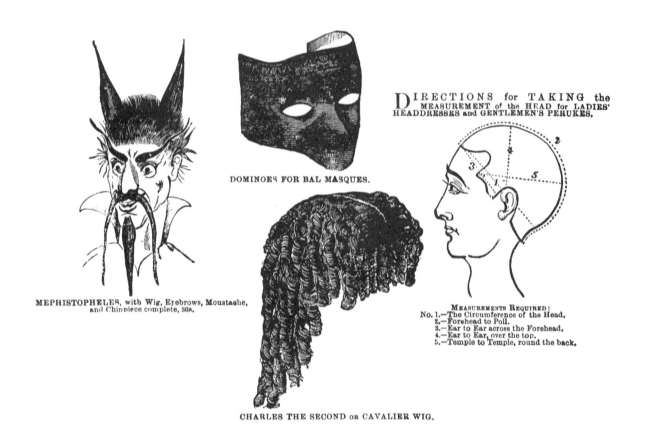

MEPHISTOPHELES, with Wig, Eyebrows, Moustache, and Chinpiece complete, 30s.

DOMINOES FOR BAL MASQUES.

DIRECTIONS for TAKING the MEASUREMENT of the HEAD for LADIES' HEADDRESSES and GENTLEMEN'S PERUKES.

MEASUREMENTS REQUIRED:
No. 1.—The Circumference of the Head.
2.—Forehead to Poll.
3.—Ear to Ear across the Forehead.
4.—Ear to Ear, over the top.
5.—Temple to Temple, round the back.

CHARLES THE SECOND or CAVALIER WIG.

The author also suggests: "Pulverize some parsley seed and use it as hair powder for three nights at the commencement of the year, and it will prevent your hair from falling.

"To make the hair grow quick, dip every morning the teeth of your comb in the juice of nettles, and comb the hair against the grain.

"To dye the hair, dissolve steel filings in good vinegar; with this vinegar, which will then resemble thick oil, wash your hair as often as you think fit, and it will make it black in a very short time. It has been asserted that the hair may be stained black by impregnating it with lard, mixed with minium and lime; the hair may likewise be turned black by different vegetable substances boiled in wine, with which the head is to be washed several times a day; but this operation ought to be continued for some time.

"To dye the hair, beard, or whiskers, take the oil of costus and myrtle, of each an ounce; mix them in a leaden mortair, add liquid pitch, juice of walnut leaves, and laudanum, of each half an ounce, gall nuts, black lead, and frankincense, of each a drachm; and a sufficient quantity of mucilage of gum arabic, infused in a concoction of nut galls. The head, whiskers, and beard, after being shaved, are to be rubbed three times a day.

"His hair will never know a fall !
'Tis ever dark and curly ;
Be wise if you wear wigs at all,
Like him adopt one early."

The man who has been younger.

HEIFFOR S ARMY RAZORS

CAN ANYTHING be perfect in creation ? Verily, as George Fox would have affirmed, it appeareth not.

The head appealing to the wig.

Can anything be perfect in creation? Verily, as George Fox would have affirmed, it appeareth not. The hairdressers' window points to the same conclusion. The bare head comes appealing to the wig, the grey whiskers to the hair dye and they suggest, as plainly as every bachelor hinted to maiden, the mutual advantages to be derived from a union. Many persons require benefit from a judicious change of hair, as any physician or wig maker can certify. Bare cheeks find here the bushy appendages they require, while the tuft, the imperial, the moustache, are at the service of the vain. Vanity and necessity are at the service of the vain. Vanity and necessity are alike patrons of the hairdresser's shop; the poor come to us with their wants, the rich with their fantasies.—The Barber's Shop, 1883.

A BARBER SHOP AT RICHMOND VIRGINIA. BY EYRE CROWE.

"To make the whiskers curl, take olive oil—1 ½ oz., spirit of Hartshorn, 1 oz. Mix. Do the hair throughly with this mixture once every two days; comb and brush well; place in order you would have, and in ringlets, wear a close tight cap over it, and it will form into natural curls.

"To prevent baldness, take extract of quinine—1 scruple, sweet almond oil—2 drachms, beef marrow—6 drachms, essence of bergamot—6 drops, Peruvian balm—8 drops. Mix with care and annoint the head on retiring.

"To remove superfluous hair—The depilatories in general use are various, possessing different degrees of strength. The mildest are parsley water, accacia juice, and the gum of ivy. It is asserted that nut oil, which many people rub the heads of children, prevents the hair from growing. The juice of the milk thistle—mixed with oil is recommended by Dr. Turner to remove the hair which grows too low upon the forehead. It is also said that the gum of the cherry tree prevents the hair from growing. A depilatory of ant's eggs is also recommended.

"To remove the hair from nostrils, take some very fine and clean wood ashes, dilute it with a little water and with the finger rub some of the mixture within the nostrils. The hair will be removed without the littlest amount of pain."

SHORT, FRONTAL FRINGE, as worn by Joseph Bonaparte

By the 1800s, another new trend to evolve—that of personal hygiene. It was noted that some of Europe's most fashionable gentlemen had started to bathe once a day and to change their underwear daily. Some critics reported that Napoleon and Josephine did just that, and they were criticized for bathing too much. To use perfume was one thing, but to bathe, was something entirely different. In a manual of etiquette published in the 1870s, "just bathing the eyes was not enough," and by the 1880s, many people were taking a weekly bath.

LEFT: MODERN VERSION OF THE BONAPARTE CUT BY PIERRE JACY.

CURLS, as worn during the Nineteenth Century.

CURLING THE HAIR WITH CURLING IRONS

Between 1810 and 1820, hair was left long enough so that it could be curled. Curls and waves were the big rage. It was said that Beau Brummell had three barbers to arrange his hair, one for the front curls, another for the side curls, and a third for the back curls. Hair was usually parted in the center. Sometimes the hair was brushed foreward from a central point on the crown. Loose waves often fell across the front of the temples. Since men's collars were high, the back hairline was usually left high for comfort's sake.

From original painting by J. R. Lambdin. Copyrighted by J. C. Tichenor, 1898.

Andrew Jackson

LONG, NATURAL HAIR, as worn by Andrew Jackson

AN ALARMING DISCOVERY. Caricature of the Nineteenth Century.

Side whiskers started to sprout into fashion early in the century. At first they were somewhat sparse, but as time went on, they increased in fullness. Slowly, but surely, another moustache movement was in the making.

A French *Manuel de la Toilete* published in 1828 supported this movement by insisting that, "La barbe est l'attribut de la virilite," and made it quite clear that its cultivation was an essential part of every gentlemen's social assets. However, the author made a definite distinction between the beard and the moustache. He considered the moustache degrading, and pomades were supposedly "exceedingly vulgar, fit only for masons and fruiterers." Instead, he recommended "egg yolk in warm water to give the hair a brilliant gloss without nits."

During the Middle Years, hair was longer than at any other time during the century. The biggest development during this era, was the gradual acceptance of beards and moustaches.

By the '30s, a few Englishmen started sprouting facial foliage. In France, the younger men who couldn't cultivate growths of their own, resorted to "falsies." The moustache required time, patience, and pampering. A special device called the moustache trainer, gave the moustache a crisp, curly appearance.

By the 1840s, hair was worn fairly full and with a side part. Although center parts were occasionally seen, they were not really fashionable. Side whiskers, which were picking up momentum, were worn down the sides of the face and under the chin.

Between the years 1850 and 1860—hair was usually waved or curled, and with a side part. However, some men preferred their hair brushed away from the face, or with a center part. Hair was heavily oiled and the use of Macassar oil gained in popularity. Side whiskers continued to sprout. In fact, by the 1850s, they were in full bloom. Although the invention of the safety razor influenced the return to clean-shaven faces, a book entitled, *The Habits of Good Society* advocated the Movement by saying, "Whatever *Punch* may say, the moustache and beard movement is one in the right direction, proving that men are beginning to appreciate beauty and to acknowledge that Nature is the best valet—Above all, the whiskers should never be curled nor pulled out to an absurd length. Still worse, is to cut them close with the scissors. The moustache should be neat and not too large, and such fopperies as cutting the points thereof or twisting them up to the fineness of needles—though patronized by the Emperor of the French—are decidedly a proof of vanity."

False hair, although it was not fashionable, was acceptable. A patent taken out in the '50s, describes a certain wig by saying: "For a Forensic wig, the curls whereof are constructed on a principle to supersede the necessity of frizzing, curling, or using hard pomatum; and for forming curls in a way not to be mauled; and also for the tails of the wig not to require tying in dressing, and further, the impossibility of any person untying them."

By the '60s, longer hair was on its way in. Hair was worn moderately waved, flattened on the crown and parted in the center. Another style en vogue, was the short Empire, worn brushed onto the forehead.

LEFT: NUMBER ONE OR BLOOD FOR BLOOD. Nineteenth Century caricature.

GERMAN MUSTACHE TRAINER. The popularity of the moustache during the 19th Century, led to the invention of the moustache binder. The moustache-binder, or schnurbartbinde, was a contraption of silk gauze, two little leather straps, and two pieces of elastic web. It looked like a bat with wings extended.

THE RIVAL WHISKERS.

By the 1870s, a clean-shaven face was, indeed, rare. Beards, moustaches, and sideburns were worn in every conceivable combination. The Harvard classes of the 1870s showed every student wearing facial fuzz.

The short, brush beard, worn with a moustache, as well as the pointed Imperial beard, were frequently seen. And, of course, the traditional Van Dyke was still going strong. The term, "goatee" was used to describe any small, chin beard.

However, side whiskers, in particular, characterized this era. Piccadilly Weepers, which hung down the sides of the face and 6" or more below the chin, enhanced the masculine image. Mutton Chops were very full at the bottom, whereas Burnsides curved across the cheeks, joining the moustache.

During the later years, beards declined in popularity, however, moustaches were almost universally worn. The Kaiser moustache, with upturned ends, captured the masculine fancy. In addition, the small, waxed moustache, which was kept under control with perfumed moustache wax, was the mark of the dude or the dandy. In the meantime, the invention of the safety razor, influenced many men to whisk off their whiskers.

From 1880 to 1890, the fashionable gent parted his hair in the middle or slightly to one side. In general, hair was worn perfectly straight and on the short side. Some men brushed their hair straight back into a modified Pompadour.

BEARD STYLES OF THE 1890 s. The Chase Manhattan Money Museum.

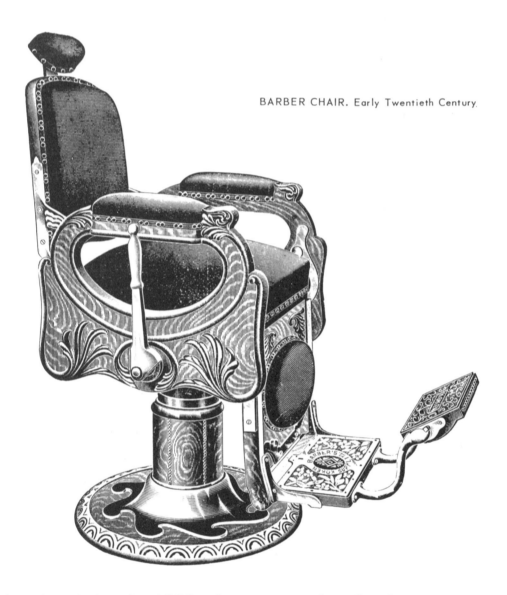

BARBER CHAIR. Early Twentieth Century.

In America, during the 1880s, the average price of a shave was ten cents. Since there were no beards to dye or trim, barbers were kept busy whisking off whiskers. In England, shaving competitions among barbers were a popular pastime. The barber, assisted by one lather boy, would try to shave as many faces as possible within one hour, without drawing any blood. At Bristol, the record was 60 faces shaved in the hour.

In America, several other factors influenced the growth of the barber industry. One was the invention of the hydraulic chair in 1890. With the hydraulic feature of raising and lowering the customer with additional comfort, this was the first step taken in shop modernization—the installation of the latest hydraulic chair. Since the late 19th century, chairs of cast iron, comfortably upholstered and so constructed that they could be adjusted, became popular.

BARBER'S COAT OF ARMS. AFTER LAMBERT, 1881.

THE BARBERING HALL OF FAME. The National Association of Barber Schools.

By the 19th Century, academies of hairdressing had been founded in several European towns. In America, the first barber college was founded in America by A. B. Moler in 1893. In these first years, the practical work of shaving, hair cutting, facial treatments, etc. was taught, "as neither the public nor the profession were ready to accept scientific treatment of the hair, skin, and scalp."

Another important development, was the formation of the Journeymen Barbers' International Union of America in Buffalo, New York, in 1887. Its forerunner, the Barbers' Protective Association was organized in 1886.

In the years that followed, the Associated Master Barbers of America became organized in November 1924, and in October 1927, the National Association of Barber Schools was established. The National Association of Barber Examiners was organized in October 1929.

THE GERMAN KAISER MOUSTACHE AND SIDE WHISKERS, as worn by William I

CHAPTER X
THE TWENTIETH CENTURY

Anything Goes

The beginning of the 20th century, was probably one of the dullest periods in the history of men's hair fashions. During the early years, short haircuts and clean-shaven faces prevailed. Anyone with hair even slightly long, was labeled a "poet" or a "musician." The center part was popular up until 1905, at which time, it was replaced by the side part. Occasionally, one would spot an old-timer wearing some side whiskers, or a distinguished-looking Van Dyke. However, moustaches were still around, with the German Kaiser moustache attracting a lot of followers.

After 1910, the hair was usually brushed away from the face into a Modified Pompadour. In 1912, an interesting article appeared in *Barber's Journal,* which gave insight as to the gentlemen of the day:

"To begin with, men like to smell sweet. Being ashamed to purchase perfume, they buy hair tonic. The shelf in front of every barber's chair looks like the buffet of a fancy drink fiend. . . . Having had his hair cut as he wants it, the man then has a shampoo. There is the egg shampoo, the prepared egg shampoo, the tar shampoo, the patent preparation shampoo, and a combination of any of these shampoos. After a man has been shampooed, he is ready for the finishing touches. All that has gone on before is just ground work for what is to follow:

THE HANDLEBAR MOUSTACHE AND WAVY HAIR, as worn during the Early Twentieth Century.

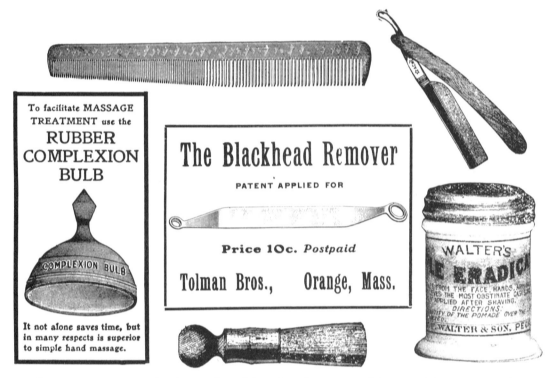

Suppose a man lacks color, his cheeks are white and have not the healthy peach bloom of the simple life. The barber rubs his cheeks with rouge or a liquid preparation and then colors them in this fashion.

Suppose the mustache is not quite brilliant enough or stiff enough. It is long enough, perhaps, but it drops and has not that jaunty, bustling, cock's comb appearance that is admired in men's mustaches. The barber rubs it with a liquid preparation which makes it brilliant, stiff, bristly, and beautiful.

Suppose any part of the facial geography is too red. The nose may be flowering like the scarlet geranium, or the ears may be too encarmined. The barber treats the offending parts with a preparation which takes the color out of the skin.

There are many other little processes, such as removing pimples, and so on, that the man orders before the barber is through with his face. When all the small details have been attended to, he usually has a rub with some sort of scented toilet water, and then the barber returns to the hair which was left tied in the towel after the shampoo. The towel is taken from the head, and the hair is found nearly dry. It may be necessary to curl the hair in front. This is done with a curling iron. Any little fancy waves the customer wants are put in and then the hair is parted. The man is now released from the chair."

TRADE PRICES

	1st Class.	2nd Class.
Hair Cut	$ .35	$ .25
Shaving	15.	.10
Beard Trimming	.50	.25
Shampooing	.50	.35
Mustache Dyeing	1.00	.50
Sea Foam	.25	.10
Singeing the Hair	.25	.25
Razor Honing	.50	.25
Neck Shaving	.10	.05
Application of Hair Tonic	.10	.10

In dyeing the hair, the charge is based on length and thickness of hair and beard, and varies from $2.00 to $10.00 for a complete job.

HAIR DRESSING.

	Fancy.	Ordinary.
Hair Dressing, Plain	$ .50	$ .25
Hair Dressing, Fancy	1.00	.75
Curling and Trimming Top Bangs	.50	.25
Shampooing Medium Length Hair	.50	.25
Shampooing Short Hair	.50	.25
Shampooing Heavy Hair	1.00	.75
Trimming and Curling Short Hair all over	1.00	.50
Singeing Long Hair all over	1.00	.50
Singeing Short Hair	.50	.25
Bleaching Medium Length, each application	1.00	.50
Bleaching Long Hair, each application	1.50	1.00
Dyeing Short Hair all over	5.00	2.00
Dyeing Medium Hair, all over	10.00	5.00
Dyeing Long, Heavy, Grey Hair, all over	25.00	15.00

A PARISIAN BARBER SHOP, 1902

By 1902, most of the better class shops in Paris charged 5 cents for a shave, 15 cents for a haircut, 15 cents for trimming the beard, 15 cents for singeing, 10 cents for shampooing, and 20 cents for dyeing the hair, whiskers, or beard. The shops that charged 10 cents for a shave and 20 cents for a haircut were usually situated along the Champs Elysees and other fashionable avenues. The two-cent shops of Paris were much more numerous than all the other classes combined. For two cents, you would get a shave; for five cents, a haircut, for another three cents, a shampoo, and the so-called "extravagant" customers, who indulged in the luxury of having their beards trimmed, their scalps singed, or their hair dyed, paid, respectively, two cents, four cents, and seven cents for the service.

In these places, no pretense was made at superficial elegance. The same lather was used for successive customers, and each towel was used at least a dozen times, and served equally for drying the face and the head.

In nearly every barber shop of Paris, the employees worked in their shirt sleeves or wore short white jackets, while the owner, who generally had a chair, was distinguished by wearing a black coat. In those places where ten cents was paid for a shave, the customer was expected to leave three cents for the man who attended to him. In five-cent shops, one and two cents were given. In the cheaper shops, no tips were even expected.

CUTTING A YOUNG MAIDEN'S HAIR AROUND 1900

BARBER'S DISH

SHOP SIGN

SHOP EMBLEM

According to the 1902 issue of *Barber's Journal,* nearly all the barbershops of Paris were on the ground floor. Only those along the main thoroughfares, or in the quarters where foreigners resided, hung out any distinguishing signs beyond those universally employed throughout France. These emblems of the trade were threefold. One consisted of a simple sign hanging in the window, bearing the word: "coiffeur." This was locally known as "the barber's ribbon." Quite as general, and more characteristic, was a little copper plate, with one side scooped out, which hung over the door. This, which was called the "barber's dish," represented the little basin, fitting snug to the neck, that was formerly used for washing the customer's face after shaving. To every man in France, the emblem said, "Shaving done here."

Another sign that was found swinging conspicuously in front of most barber shops in Paris told quite a different story. It was a big gilt ball from which was suspended a wide-spreading tuft of horsehair. This emblem meant, "ladies' barber and hairdresser."

In all the better shops in Paris, soaps, perfumes, and general toiletries were sold. One in every five barbers in Paris was the inventor of a scalp cleaner, hair restorer, or hair dye.

Many of the shops also made a specialty of ironing the silk hats of customers, for which a charge of five cents was made. This was just about one half of what it would have cost at a hatter's. A fair proportion of the Paris barbers were also wigmakers, but as a general thing, they dealt only in toupees, or half wigs. All barbers, however, holding the degree of professor, were required to know how to make wigs, as well as how to arrange ladies' hair in any current fashion.

FIGURE NO. 22.

Plate No. 22. This plate shows long hair as worn by musicians, elocutionists, lecturers, preachers, and other professional men.

The hair is about four inches long all over the head and shingled around the edges down to one and one-half inches. It is cut very low down on the neck to almost reach down to the coat collar.

It may be worn parted in the centre, side, or brushed back without parting, German student style.

The style becomes most any shaped head, but is more becoming to small heads and long necks.

TWO PARISIAN BARBER CHAIRS   APPARATUS FOR DRYING HAIR WITH HOT AIR

In the better shops, the journeyman received from 80 cents to $1.25 a day, not including tips, which in some places, amounted to nearly double their wages. The majority of shops opened for business at 8:00 am, except on Saturdays, when the closing hour was 10 o'clock. The rule on Sundays was to close at noon, but an occasional place kept open until 4 o'clock. On important holidays, the barber shops were almost the only business houses in the city open until late in the afternoon.

All tips were pooled. All the coins that went into the metal box were regarded as forming a common pool, which were divided regularly every night among all the journeymen of the shop. The instant a coin was heard falling into the tip box, the entire staff would come forth with a chorus of "merci, monsieur."

In general appearance, a first-class barber shop in Paris differed very little from one in New York, or any other American city. The toilet finishings were practically the same. Around three walls of the salon extended a row of stationary washstands, usually in white, red, or yellow marble, all equipped with ornamental metal spigots. Above the basins and fronting the chairs were mirrors. The chief difference here were the chairs. Instead of the American richly-upholstered chairs with adaptable head-rests, a comfortable extension for the feet, and the whole object so pivoted that it could be turned without the exercise of the least effort, the barber "fauteuil" in Paris was simply a good-sided arm chair of plain, uncarved wood, with the seat and back of plaited cane. The head rest consisted of a hard wooden band joined on to a groove at the back of the chair. This band could be moved three or four inches up or down and wherever it was, it stretched the customer's neck in a most uncomfortable fashion, besides causing a sensation at the back of the head similar to what would occur, should the client sleep on an iron pillow.

FIGURE NO. 23.

Figure No. 23 Represents the Pompadour Cut.

The pompadour illustrated above (No. 23) while not so much employed as formerly, is nevertheless still much in vogue among a certain class. In making this cut, the hair is dampened and a little pomade or vaseline is rubbed well into the hair to make it lay or brush up while the line of trimming is being struck. This line should taper only slightly downward from the front to the crown or back.

FRONT VIEW of the boyish bob

BACK VIEW showing inverted hairline

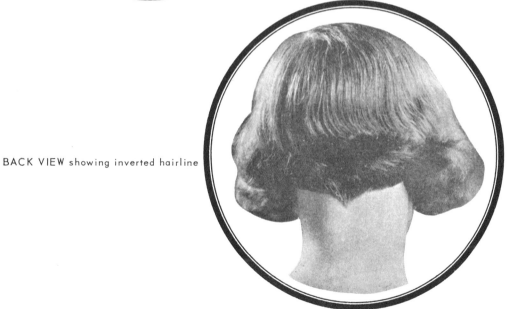

Between 1918 and 1925, women invaded barber shops for the "scandalous" boyish bob. The boyish bob, French bob, straight bob, shingle, Castle Bob, and Valentine bob, were the fashion favorites. "Barbers," according to the *Barber's Journal*, "did not particularly rave over the pleasure of cutting a fair maiden's hair, although they were glad to have the business." They said, "It was the most impersonal operation in the world. If Prince Charming, himself, were the barber, he would be ignored save as a useful instrument by the fair one getting her hair bobbed for the first time. Her heart is always solely in the bob and her eyes on the mirror's changing picture."

1919 AMERICAN

1933 AMERICAN

1948 AMERICAN

1956 AMERICAN

John Verdura

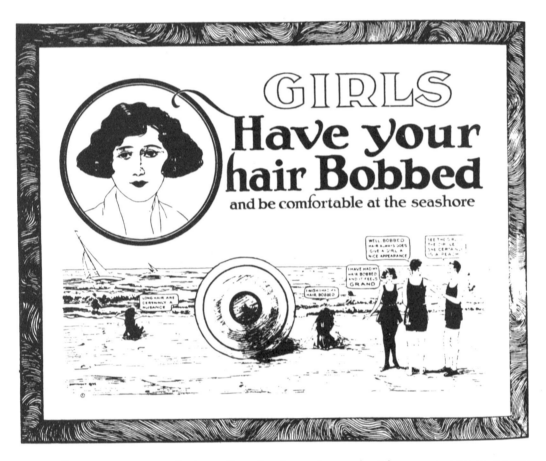

Ladies were not only invading barber shops, but in some cases, were actually taking over as lady barbers:

At a gathering of master barbers in 1923, the statement was made that, "The lady tonsorialist was more successful in the trade than the masculine knight of the razor." According to the Master Barbers, "When the shoe drummer from St. Louis gets into the chair of the lady barber, she is likely to shoot him for the whole works. He came in for a quick shave, but he goes out with a shampoo, a massage, and a tonic treatment. He is perfumed and anointed like one of the kings of Israel. Instead of coughing up a dime for a once-over, he has spent $2 of the firm's money for the doubtful joy of having his head caressed by a buxom barberess. Whether she can do as good a job as him, the lady barber gets the money."

In the meantime, London, being the arbitrator of fashion, declared, "delicate side whiskers were again coming into fashion in the West End of London, England. They were not so pronounced as in the early Victorian "face flap," but they were short and flimsy, with a gentle curl inward from the ear."

THE CHARLIE CHAPLIN MOUSTACHE OF THE 1920 s

Marcelling

Another trend reported by trade journals was an increased interest in the use of cosmetics for men. According to one authority, "Today, wrinkles are removed from the face by means of a mud that draws them out, massage makes the face more cleanly and there are many articles sold by barbers for the hair. Some of these are supposed to grow hair on a billiard ball."

Hairpieces, by the way, were making inroads in the American male market. According to an advertisement in *Barber's Journal*, dated 1922, one manufacturer was successfully selling toupees at $15.00 each, and guaranteeing to match any shade of hair. It was also during the 20s, that the term, "hairstylist," was first noticed. A hairstylist was described as a person who offered himself as an expert in the designing and dressing of hair styles. By the 1930s, it was firmly established.

In an interview with a foreign correspondent for *Barber's Journal*, dated November 1923, it was reported: "The barbers in England wear long, black coats that give them a sort of funereal aspect, and they seldom stop to brush the hair from their clothes after a haircut has been administered. Just to show how behind the times they are in the foreign barber shops, let us look at the way in which they prepare for shaving. Instead of using water, they use a sponge for the second shave. This is horribly unsanitary and could not be tolerated in any of the less sanitary shops here in America.

"In France," according to the writer, "the barbers depend more for a living upon the sale of perfumeries, pomade, and hair tonics than upon the patronage of their instructors. Another thing that is sold extensively in the barber shops of France and Germany are lathering brushes, and there is considerable profit for the customer in it."

As far as American barber shops were concerned, a visitor from abroad said, "Barber shops are much more luxurious; they take much more money from each individual customer, one of the principal barber shops impressing me that on an average a customer spends 66 cents, this would surprise our English trade."

The Much Misunderstood Manicurist

To begin with, I will state that a manicurist is a person whose occupation is to improve the appearance of the hands and nails. Many things have been said of the manicurist, some of the comments not being at all complimentary, as many seem to believe that she is a hot-house product with only a good working knowledge of cosmetics and hair dyes; that she is a mischievious girl who is forever preying on men and whose favorite pastime is the breaking up of homes.

The manicurist's experience with men are many and varied. It is her business to be polite and agreeable. Of course, these qualities are often mistaken by the silly Don Juan for sentiments inspired by his ir-resistability, and it is really amusing to what extent the vanity of these men fools them, but being educated in the good school of common sense, she pays no attention to such simpletons. One cannot be blamed for using a little heavy artillery in the form of painting, powder, and lipstick.

As for the many imputations that she preys upon rich men—I will say that, very often, men of wealth fall for the manicurist, and why not? If she is an accomplished and well-bred lady, if she possesses the qualities that rich men desire and admire in women, why shouldn't she marry a wealthy man?

MOUSTACHE AND BEARD STYLES AROUND 1900.

Another interesting innovation, was the moustache cup. The moustache cup contained a china bridge half-way across the inside. This bridge held back the moustache and prevented it from getting wet, as the wearer drank its contents.

During these early years, the *Barber's Journal* took a firm stand on the wearing of perfumes. According to one editorial, "No longer are men forbidden the privilege of carrying about them any aroma save that of tobacco. Dame fashion now decrees that they may use perfumes once more. King David was never considered an effeminate man, yet, he had his perfumes and scented apparel. Julius Caesar, although fond of fragrance about his person, lacked nothing in courage, or greatness, and nobody ever looked upon General Grant as any less a warrior because he liked the perfumes to which men for ages have been accustomed, and the objection to which, is as much an affectation as the objection to the scent of flowers."

FANCY COLOGNE BOTTLES OF THE EARLY TWENTIETH CENTURY.

AMERICAN BARBER, 1902

The barber during these early years, didn't have the numerous products available to him today. In fact, he looked to books on the *Art of Barbering* by E. M. Robinson for some recipes for the best, cheapest, and most easily prepared products. For example, to make brown hair dye, the author suggests: "Take four pounds of green walnut hulls. Put them in one and one-half gallons soft water and boil down to three pints. Strain off through cloth until clear of sediment. To one quart of this add one quart alcohol, and three ounces glycerine. Use as other restorers, once a day until the desired shade is obtained. The hulls should be gathered in August."

To make pomade, Mr. Robinson suggested that the barber have a butcher get him some fine leaf lard and some of the finest suet, which should be taken from young animals. He was told to pour it into a porcelain vessel and strain. The recipe given was as follows: "Take lard, 1 pound, and tallow, 1 pound. Mix them, heat gently, and cook for one hour over a slow fire; remove and let stand a few minutes to settle; now pour off carefully. When almost cold, add some suitable perfume, say Oil of Bergamot 4 drachms, Oil of Lemon 3 drachms, Oil of Cassia, 2 drachms, Oil of Nutmeg 75 drops. Mix thoroughly with the pomade and pour into small jars."

UPTURNED MOUSTACHE, AND POINTED BEARD OF EARLY TWENTIETH CENTURY.

SINGEING.

On the subject of beards and moustaches, Mr. Robinson went on to say; "A handsome man is handsomer with the proper style of beard, and homely or coarse features are softened by the wearing of some becoming whiskers, which detract from the coarseness of the features. A full beard when properly trimmed, becomes most every man, but when it does not grow full enough, or of any even thickness, it may be shaven in various styles. The short, broad face is improved by a chin beard, while a long, thin face is broadened and appears shorter by wearing side whiskers. A moustache shades off a large nose, also covers a homely mouth, bad teeth, and thick lips. The Imperial (or goatee) is trying to certain types of faces, although it has been extensively worn and is still used by many." The author also gives some advice on dressing a moustache: A moustache should always be dressed or rolled to give it a natural, easy appearance. When it is rolled on paper or curled with an iron or slate pencil, it should be combed out in an easy and natural way. Artificial appearance should always be avoided. It is very poor taste to leave the moustache rolled up in a bunch."

Singeing was also practiced on persons "whose hair was of fine texture, inclined to brittleness and of sparing growth and density. By singeing, the ends of the hair were supposed to become hermetically sealed, and to retain all the natural oil, that would, to some degree, otherwise leak out of the hair, and thereby rob the sabaceous glands and their hair follicles of the nutriment requisite to its growth and development."

ABOVE: LUSTRE, as popularized by George Raft.

By the 1920s, lustre, as popularized by Rudolph Valentino and George Raft, made fashion news. The big rage was flat, plastered-down hair. In addition, there was a vogue for artificial-looking waves. It was reported in June 1922 that the marcel wave for men was the latest fad for men. According to an expert waver from Boston, "The male sex submits to the ordeal of the curling iron with all the stoicism of an Indian. Women sometimes wiggle about and cringe at the too near approach of the hot tongs, but not so the men. In their anxiety to beautify themselves, they risk burning without a thought." The most distressing development was the military haircut in which the head was clipped close all around, leaving the hairline at approximately eyebrow level. This resembled the bowl cut of the early 15th century, except the hair on top was very closely-cropped. This style, which was worn by soldiers, as well as civilians, lasted for several years.

LEFT: THE FLAT, PLASTERED DOWN LOOK OF RUDOLPH VALENTINO.

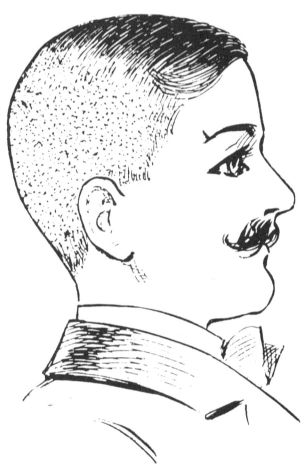

THE CLIPPER CUT. Early Twentieth Century.

According to a report in *Barber's Journal*, dated 1923, "The prevalence of the short cut in the army affected civilian haircuts. The method was comparatively simple; the clippers were applied at the back and the sides and an appearance like a close-clipped rye field was obtained. The war having been fought, the tendency has swung in the other direction. The elite, it seems, were asking for the clippers only in the back and demanding the shears for the sides. The Rudolph Valentino burnside had become a fixture. The Pompadour, first brought in by Madame (not Monsieur, strangely enough) Pompadour, continued, with little hope of checking it. A remarkable phenomenon was the swing towards the part-in-the-middle. The front wave was still worn by many young men. The moustache was steadily declining in popularity. Among the older generation, the tradition of the prophetic beards of grandsires still clung in the shape of the moustache, but the younger generation had forgotten grandpa, and such moustaches which were worn had little honor to him."

NATURALLY WAVY HAIR, as worn by Rudy Vallee.

WAVY HAIR, as worn by Cary Grant

By the 1930s, the patent-leather look was considered passe. In addition, the Pompadour was no longer fashionable. Any natural wave was allowed to have its way, rather than be slicked down with any heavy pomade. Moustaches, on the somewhat conservative side, were still popular among older men. Beards, especially in America, were considered outdated. The biggest trend was the no-part hairstyle, which revealed the contour of the head.

In the meantime, trade journals encouraged barbers to start a toupee business, to continue promoting facials, and to consider haircoloring as a special service.

LEFT: THE PENCIL-LINE MOUSTACHE AND OFF-CENTER PART OF ROBERT TAYLOR.

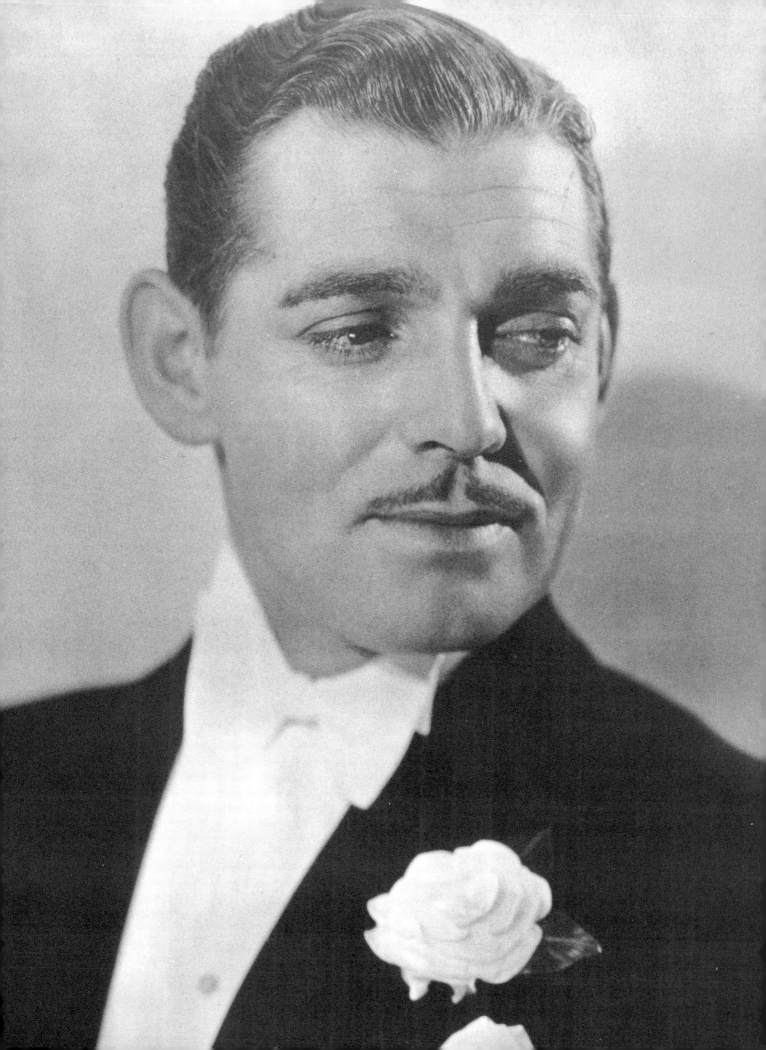

A MODERN VERSION OF THE CLARK GABLE MOUSTACHE. Photo: Kenn Duncan.

By the 1940s, wavy hair was not only acceptable, but highly fashionable, as well. Even when the hair was worn straight, barbers encouraged any hidden wave. During this era, the trend-setters were the movie stars, whose ideas were copied by teenagers and college students everywhere. Although beards were still not considered fashionable, moustaches, which ranged from the pointy, waxy type to the Clark Gable variety, were seen. The trend towards slightly longer hair began in the '40s, when fullness was required at both the sides and top. By 1946, the most popular styles revealed more height in front and slightly longer sides. However, since these were still the war years, the crewcut which was worn by so many servicemen, encouraged some civilians to adopt the trend. The handlebar moustache, a moustache with ends like the handlebar of a bicycle, was worn by many men in the Royal Air Force.

In the meantime, barbers started to do more to enhance the masculine image. In 1946, a regular contributor to *Barber's Journal,* suggested that the word "haircut" be changed to "hairshaping" and the word "barber shop," be changed to "gentlemen's beauty salon." It was recommended that a number of different definitions be used in conveying the word, "hairstyling" to the public.

LEFT: THE CLARK GABLE MOUSTACHE of 1936.

TAB HUNTER wearing the Crew Cut of the 1950s. Courtesy of Warner Bros.

After the Second World War ended, the "Teddy Boys" with their Edwardian style of dress, looked for more individuality in hairstyles. The movement towards longer hair started to creep in by the early '50s. Hairstyles varied from the Elvis Presley to the Crew Cut to the Caesar Cut. Trade journals featured the Flat Top as being "real cool," and the Hollywood, or the Tony Curtis style for the man who wanted the look of longer hair. The Crew Cut, which started out as a college favorite, was also known as the G.I. Cut. As the hair was shown slightly longer and somewhat tousled, it became a Feather Crew, and more recently, the Ivy League. The Brush Cut, a style which was cut short at the back, and longer on top, enjoyed some popularity in America, France, and England.

LEFT: THE TONY CURTIS STYLE OF THE 1950s, for the man who wanted the look of longer hair. Courtesy of M-G-M.

ABOVE: THE MEXICAN ZAPATA MOUSTACHE OF THE 1950s, as worn by Marlon Brando. RIGHT: A MODERN VERSION OF THE MEXICAN ZAPATA MOUSTACHE. Style by Carl Caramanna. Photo: Kenn Duncan (Courtesy of *Men's Hairstylist & Barber's Journal*).

The Manchester Guardian in March 1954 reported on the revival of interest in male hairdressing by saying: "Some men are even keener than women. Youths in their teens and early twenties are keenest on the styles of Tony Curtis 'one curl at the front and occasionally a bunch of curls.' A variation of that is the Duck's Anatomy which had to be re-named because some critics called it by a slang expression, the District Attorney." The Guardian goes on to say, "Hair is fashioned to suit the client's type of face and personality. The crew cut (from the lumber-jacks of Canada) can be rendered round, square, British, or American. The younger men are going in for more elaborate hairdo's, partly as a revolt against the standardization that they have to submit to in the forces, but the mass of men are simply becoming more hair-conscious."

An English source also reported that "Some of the older men in the suburbs no longer seek a simple back and sides, but sit back for such improvements as permanent waving, silver and gilt threads, tipped gilt ends, and hair dyes which include such colors as red, blonde, brown, or whatever else suits their fancy."

Prices for male hairdressing were not cheap. A so-called Dale Robertson in England cost 15 shillings. Among other fashionable styles were The Director, which featured a slight wave on the crown of the head, The Academician, which had a high side part, and other American styles such as The Flying Saucer and the Droop Snoot, which featured a horizontal part across the head from ear to ear.

In America, an increase in the number of beards was noted by *Barber's Journal*, when they reported: "New York subway riders have stopped staring at men who wear beards . . . they are used to them now. All around the town, the beard has come into its own." Hairy faces are now familiar on Madison Avenue, on college campuses, backstage at off-Broadway theaters, and in Greenwich Village."

In addition, tinting and blow waving started gaining in importance. Dryers were designed for wind waving, blow-waving, and air waving. The big emphasis was on the appointment system of barbering, and the emergence of the professional hairstylist. An increased interest in hairpieces, haircoloring, and hair straightening was also evident. The First Annual International Barber & Men's Hairstylist Show in November 1958 reportedly drew more than 1,000 barbers who were interested in men's hairstyling.

LEFT: ELVIS PRESLEY WEARING LONG SIDEBURNS AND HAIR PULLED DOWN OVER THE FOREHEAD.

THE CAESAR CUT, as worn by Marlon Brando

The trends developed in the '50s, were carried over into the early '60s. In addition, there was an increased interest in styles. Hair was still being worn relatively short, although there was a tendency to create styles which gave the illusion of more length. By 1963, the no part hairstyle gained in popularity. The Caesar Cut, which was a college favorite and the Empire, reflected the trend towards more frontal fringe. However, the flat-top, also known as the California Cut, the Detroit Cut, and the Dutch cut, was still being worn in some parts of the country.

LEFT: THE TREND TOWARDS BEARD-GROWING, as evidenced during the late 1960s. Artistic beard design of 1967 by Vivi Avila. Photo: David Valenzuela.

1966 AMERICAN

AMERICAN TEENAGER

AMERICAN 1965

AMERICAN TEENAGER
1967

John Verdura

LONG HAIR, as worn by the Beatles

The 1960s witnessed a number of revolutionary changes in the men's hairstyling industry. *Barber's Journal,* the industry's leading trade publication, reflected the trend to men's hairstyling when it changed its name to *Men's Hairstylist* in November 1964. The reason for the change was given as follows:

"A good barber is no longer just a barber. He's a hair stylist. Actually, he's more than a men's hairstylist, he's a men's grooming specialist, because his services go beyond hairstyling. He knows hair coloring. He knows how to specify, cut, style and instruct a man on the proper use of a hairpiece. He knows how to prescribe the correct partial hairpiece for the open area on each man's top. He knows that just being available for a haircut isn't being in business as a stylist. He knows that he must be a businessman, as well as a professional. He knows that he must promote because he must be more than a service. Today's man with shears, razor, color and hairpiece can never be characterized as just a barber. His customers don't think of him that way. He doesn't think of himself that way. A publication entitled, *The Barber's Journal* does not mirror his image any longer."

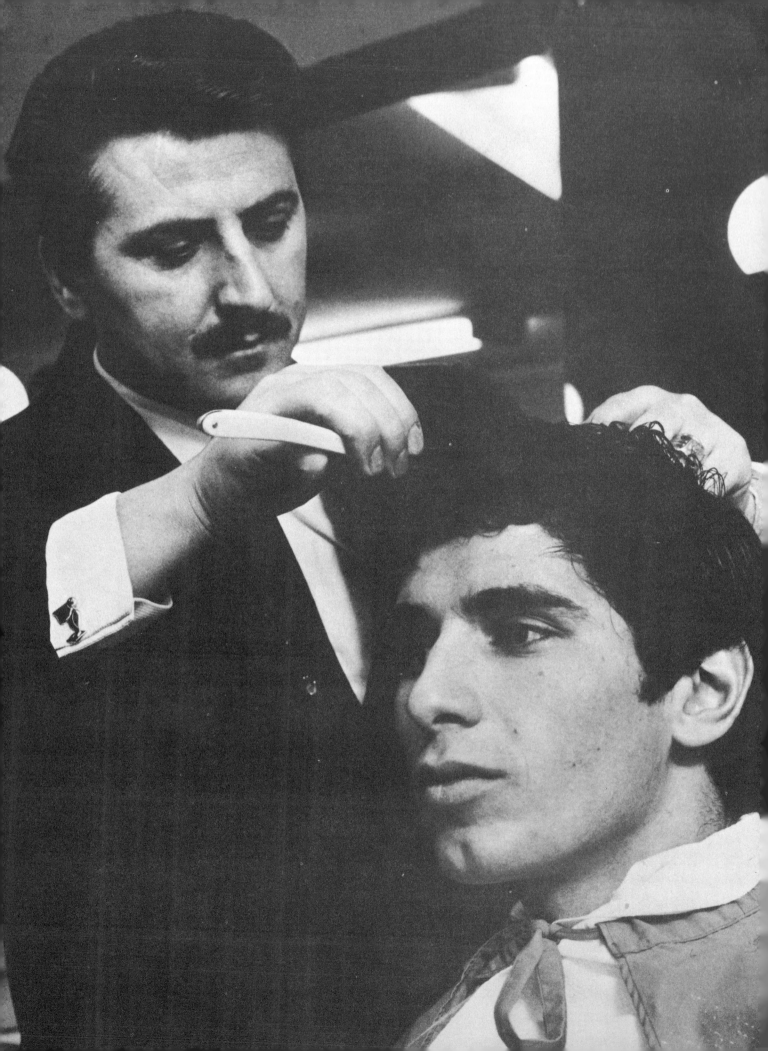

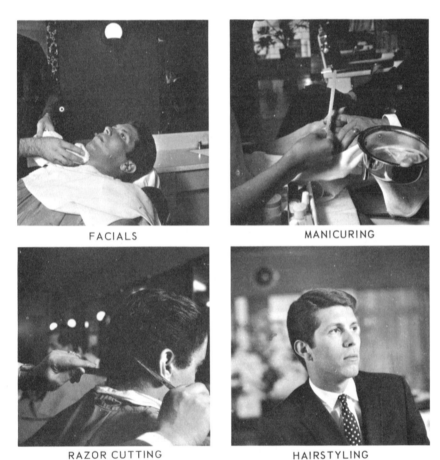

FACIALS

MANICURING

RAZOR CUTTING

HAIRSTYLING

As a result, the word, "men's hairstylist," has come to mean an expert in the designing and dressing of hairstyles. By putting into effect the principles of artistic hairstyling—symmetry, balance, harmony, proportion, and design, the hair-stylist creates a personalized style for each of his clients. For example, he takes into consideration, the amount and length of a man's hair, his head contour, hairline, and other characteristics such as a low forehead, high cheekbones, heavy jowls, etc. The result is a highly individualized style, which is not only flattering, but practical, as well. Consequently, men's hairstyling salons have opened up all over the world, in keeping with this new concept. Today, the full service shop offers such services as pedicures, shoe shines, hair removal, body massage, shaving, facials, eyebrow coloring and shaping, haircutting, razor cuts, hairstyling, shampoos, hair straightening, hair coloring, scalp treatments, manicuring, hairpiece fitting, cleaning, and servicing, hair conditioning, make-up, mustache and beard trimming, and body waving.

LEFT: ROGER OF NEW YORK employing the French method of razor cutting.

MOUSTACHE CHART OF 1967.

Perhaps the most notable development during the 1960s, has been the increase in beards, moustaches, and sideburns. The April 1967 issue of *Men's Hairstylist* featured several beard styles and instructed hairstylists on how to create artistic beard designs. Consequently, in October 1967, another Moustache Movement was predicted. It was also in this issue that an instant beard kit was introduced, which eventually revolutionized the entire industry. By 1969, sideburns, which ranged from the long, straight variety to the curved Sassoons to the exaggerated Mutton Chops, swung into fashion. Hair weaving, as well as high-fashion hairpieces, offered a modern approach to balding clients.

LEFT: WRAP-AROUND BEARD DESIGN by Vivi Avila. Photo: David Valenzuela.

WILD, UNTAMED HAIR, as seen in wig for the musical, HAIR. By Rosy Carita of Paris.

The latest trends indicate a move towards curly hair. Waves, whether acquired through the use of a modern curling iron, or a permanent wave, are starting to make a comeback. Illusion styling, which is used to camouflage receding hairlines, also takes on added importance. But, this is only the beginning. Turn to Page 211 for some futuristic predictions.

LEFT: THE TREND TOWARDS LONGER HAIR, as evidenced by this hairstyle which extends over the ears. Style by Joseph Donahue. Photo: Joseph Griffith. Courtesy of *Men's Hairstylist & Barber's Journal*.

CHAPTER XI
THE YEAR 2001

Look Into My Crystal Ball

By the Year 2001, what will the man on the moon look like? Will a lunar "hippie" protest by means of a closely-shaved scalp, and will a balding Astro flash a pair of false eyebrows to offset his full magnetic wig?

According to Coiffure Masculine, by the Year 2001, 75% of the male population will be wearing wigs. However, these wigs will be worn primarily as fashion accessories, rather than to conceal baldness. These wigs, in no sense, will be a camouflage for natural hair. On the contrary, they will be a matter of great personal pride. Wigs for different occasions will appear on the fashion scene. For example, there will be wigs for work, wigs for dress, wigs for dancing, etc. Since there will be considerable freedom of choice, some wigs will be curly, some almost frizzy, but in general, deep waves and natural lines will be important.

LEFT: FULL-FASHIONED WIGS FOR THE YEAR 2001. Fashions by Steve Lyons of the Zoo. Wigs by Roger of New York. Photos: Courtesy of *Men's Hairstylist & Barber's Journal.*

In addition, it is predicted that by the Year 2001, baldness will be obsolete. Men will no longer accept baldness as a natural state of affairs. In the first stages of baldness, corners or "temple ticklers," as they are now called, will be used to camouflage receding hairlines. Black and brown color sprays will be used to darken balding areas, too.

For the more advanced stages of baldness, hairpieces, which will be put on like a hat, will be used. However, unlike today's hairpieces which are affixed with glue and tape, hairpieces in the future will be secured almost magnetically with a chemically-treated synthetic fibre.

It is also pointed out that due to the great popularity of hi-fashion wigs, the hair, whenever it is seen in its natural state, will be dressed to look like a wig. In general, hair will be longer and fuller than it is worn today. However, color will be the most important aspect of men's hairstyling. It is estimated that by the year 2001, 75% of the male population will resort to hair coloring of some kind—whether it's a color spray to camouflage balding areas, or a blue rinse to highlight grey hair, or a permanent hair lightener which will transform a brunette into a blond. Note: For those fashion-conscious men who wear wigs on a constant basis, very short haircuts, and even shaved heads will prevail.

LEFT: BLOND WIG WITH PASTE-ON SIDEBURNS AND MOUSTACHE. Fashions by Steve Lyons of The Zoo. Wigs by Roger of New York. Courtesy of Men's Hairstylist & Barber's Journal.

In addition, make-up for men, says Coiffure Masculine, will not only be acceptable, but highly fashionable in the future. Skin care problems will be discussed among men as freely as they discuss the stock market or a baseball game today. It is further predicted, that by the Year 2001, there will be a great deal of emphasis on the eyes. In fact, false eyebrows to match different colored wigs will appear. Some manufacturers will even introduce false eyelashes for men. Men with spare eyelashes and very light eyelashes, will be particularly interested in these items. In addition, the false moustache, which has gained so much popularity today, will reappear on the fashion scene. However, this time, rather than the big, bushy types, the highly-waxed variety, will take over.

LEFT: THE LOOK OF THE FUTURE — A CURLY STRETCH WIG FOR MEN. Photo: Kenn Duncan. Courtesy of Men's Hairstylist & Barber's Journal.

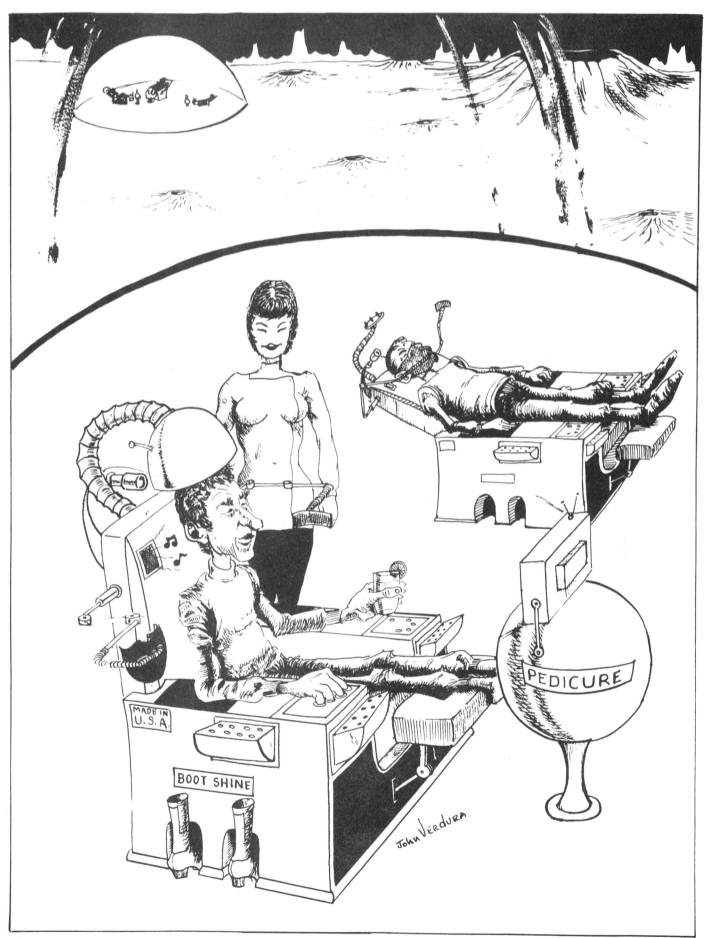

ABOVE: MEN'S HAIRSTYLING SALON FOR THE YEAR 2001. Note the automatic shaving devices, pedicure machines, and manicuring equipment.

LEFT: UP-TURNED MOUSTACHE AND PIG-TAILS. Wigs by Roger of New York. Photo: *Men's Hairstylist & Barber's Journal.*

CHAPTER XII
A COMPLETE GUIDE TO HAIR CARE FOR MEN

1. Finding The Right Hairstyle.

Finding the *right* hairstyle, depends upon finding the *right* hairstylist. As the expert in the field, he has mastered the fundamentals of artistic hair design. Therefore, he can combine the elements of symmetry, balance, harmony, rhythm, and proportion, for the most flattering effect.

The first consideration is your basic face shape. Do you have an oval face . . . a round face . . . a square face . . . or a long face?

The oval face is the ideal face. This type of face can wear practically any hairstyle. Stick to simple, uncluttered lines, those which reveal perfect contours.

The round face has a wide forehead, rounded hairline, and curved jawbones. The most flattering style is one which maximizes the top hair and breaks down the rounded look. Stay away from center parts and long sideburns.

The square face has a wide forehead, squarish hairline, and squarish jawbones. Maximize the hair at the sides and leave the hair on top reasonably full. Avoid flat hairstyles and closely-cropped sides.

The long, thin face is either oblong or angular. In razor cutting the hair, the sides are kept both long and full. The top of the hair is left on the short side to reduce the length of the face. Never wear exaggerated sideburns.

LEFT: THE SHORT, EMPIRE. Hairstyle by Roger of New York. Photo: Kenn Duncan. Courtesy of *Men's Hairstylist & Barber's Journal.*

THE 5 IN 1 HAIRSTYLE

STYLE NO. 1—This style places emphasis on the full sweep across the front ot the forehead. Note the long sideburns which reflect a very definite European influence.

STYLE NO. 2—The Empire, with its soft, free-flowing lines, reflects the trend towards more frontal fringe.

STYLE NO. 3—The Casual Look, with a deliberately natural feeling, is a perfect complement to today's more casual way of life.

STYLE NO. 4—The conservative image, with an interesting semi-part, is best conveyed by this well-balanced hairstyle.

STYLE NO. 5—This smooth, uncluttered silhouette, is directed away from the face, to draw attention to strong contours.

THE SAME MAN WEARING TWO DIFFERENT HAIRSTYLES

Your next consideration involves structural defects. Do you have a long nose . . . a recessive chin . . . dominant jaws . . . or prominent ears? The right hairstyle will minimize these conditions.

A long nose looks less prominent with full, frontal lines. An interesting side part often detracts from the long nose. In general, soft, sweeping lines soften the profile.

A recessive chin looks less recessive with an attractive goatee. A chin beard balances a weak chin. Avoid any exaggerated hairstyles which extend beyond the front hairline, creating an even greater imbalance. Dominant jaws, on the other hand, look more balanced, when offset with full, frontal hair.

Prominent ears look closer to the face, when the hair around the ears is left long and full. Avoid the closely-cropped look.

In addition, a low forehead needs an off-the-face hairstyle for better balance, whereas a high forehead benefits from a long, full style, especially across the front hairline.

Other considerations include your personality, your physique, and your position. It stands to reason that an outgoing creative type who carries himself with authority, could probably handle an avant-garde Grecian cut, whereas, a conservative businessman with a somewhat reserved personality, would look out of place in the same hairstyle. In addition, the short man who thinks he will look much taller by wearing an oversized pompadour, is just fooling himself. Although a certain amount of top hair will enhance his height, anything which is too extreme, will make him look out of proportion.

LEFT: THE FIVE-IN-ONE HAIRSTYLE. FIVE DIFFERENT STYLES FROM ONE BASIC CUT. Styles by Roger of New York. Sketches by Joyce Kunsch.

2. Beards, Moustaches, And Sideburns.

Beards, moustaches, and sideburns can also be used to balance a less-than-perfect face. For example, the moustache is a great way to camouflage a prominent nose, minimize a protruding lip, or break down an extremely flat profile. A beard can cover a scar or conceal a bad skin condition.

For the man with a short, round face, and heavy facial features, a wide English moustache is recommended. The round face may be lengthened by wearing a full, wrap-around beard which cuts the width of the face at its broadest point, or a pointed Imperial beard. Stay away from short sideburns or very thick beards as they emphasize rounded contours.

A thin, pencil-line moustache flatters the long, narrow face. When the upper lip is somewhat long, the ends of the moustache should be dropped. Long sideburns can be used effectively to fill out sunken cheeks. Any facial hair which gives width to the lower portion of the face, is flattering.

LEFT: ARTISTIC BEARD DESIGN by Vivi Avila. Photo: David Valenzuela.

To cultivate a beard or moustache, first allow a sufficient amount of growth. Then seek the advice of a good hairstylist. Periodic visits to a hairstylist will guarantee a well-groomed beard and moustache. Most stylists recommend a trim at least every two weeks. When doing it yourself, remember that the bottom of the moustache must be trimmed first. Too many men start to trim at the top, and before they know it, there's no moustache left. A moustache will look neat as long as it never projects over the edge of the upper lip. Many stylists recommend the use of a moustache wax. The moustache wax will control unruly ends. In addition, hair spray will give it a little extra stiffness.

If you decide to cultivate longer sideburns, they should be allowed to grow in slowly—about 1/4" at a time. Sideburns should be left full around the ears. Don't have them trimmed too close. If you can't grow the kind of sideburns you'd like to have, you might experiment with a pair of "falsies." False beards, moustaches, and sideburns, can be worn strictly for fun, or to create a completely new image. Instant facial fuzz is especially handy when you have neither the time, nor the patience to cultivate a growth of your own.

LEFT: FALSE MOUSTACHE AND CONSERVATIVE CUT by Roger of New York. Photo: Kenn Duncan (Courtesy of *Men's Hairstylist & Barber's Journal*).

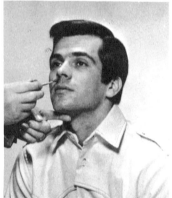

To apply false beards, moustaches, and sideburns, follow these easy steps:

The Moustache—Trim the excess lace close to the hairline, being careful not to cut into the hairline. Place the moustache above the center of the upper lip. Using an eyebrow pencil, trace the outline of the moustache. Apply a sufficient amount of spirit gum within the marks outlined by the pencil. Blot off any excess spirit gum with a lint-free cloth. Place the moustache above the center of the upper lip, and press down with the fingers, being careful to leave 1/8" between the moustache and the upper lip. Exercise a light amount of pressure on each side for about 10 to 15 seconds. If necessary, trim the moustache according to the face.

The Goatee—Trim the excess lace close to the hairline, being careful not to cut into the hairline. Place the goatee in the center of the chin so that it is 1/4" below the lower lip. Be sure that the two points of the goatee fall directly below the corners of the lip. Using an eyebrow pencil, trace the outline of the goatee. Apply a sufficient amount of spirit gum within the marks outlined by the pencil. Place the goatee in the center of the chin so that it is 1/4" below the lower lip and press down with the fingers. Exercise a light amount of pressure on all sides for about 10 to 20 seconds. If necessary, trim the goatee according to the face.

The Full Beard—To apply a full beard, follow the same method outlined for the moustache and goatee, however, in positioning the full beard, be sure to place it so that the natural hair covers the ends of the beard.

Sideburns—To apply sideburns, follow the same procedure outlined above. To remove any of the above facial pieces, use rubbing alcohol.

LEFT: THE ZHIVAGO LOOK featuring 3/4 part and instant facial foliage by Roger of New York. Photo: Kenn Duncan (Courtesy of *Men's Hairstylist & Barber's Journal*).

3. Maintaining Healthy Hair

Dry hair, which is dull, and often accompanied by dandruff, requires special care. Daily brushing is recommended to stimulate the flow of natural oils. Use a special shampoo for dry hair. Conditioners which contain lanolin will aid your condition. A hot-oil treatment is also recommended to replenish natural oils.

Oily hair is often difficult to handle. It separates easily, and feels greasy a day or two after you've had it styled. Shampoo your hair as often as possible with a special shampoo designed to correct this condition. It may even be necessary to shampoo your hair daily, if the oiliness is really excessive. Daily brushing is also recommended to distribute natural oils.

Stimulation plays a very important role in the treatment of dandruff. Daily brushing, as well as regular massaging, will help normalize your condition. Use special formulated shampoos for dandruff. Be sure to rinse carefully. Keep combs and brushes extra clean. For serious cases of dandruff, see your dermatologist.

Thick hair, although it is usually healthy hair, is very often unmanageable. It is even more difficult to handle if it is bushy and wiry. A good haircut is extremely important with this type of hair. In addition, cream rinses which add softness, and hair sprays which control unruly locks, are also recommended.

Fine, limp hair needs special handling. Use only a soft bristle brush for brushing your hair. Shampoo as often as necessary, using a conditioner instead of a cream rinse. Protein conditioners are especially beneficial. Use a setting lotion prior to styling. For longer-lasting results, try a body wave.

LEFT: THE CASUAL, NATURAL LOOK by Roger of New York. Photo: Kenn Duncan. Courtesy of *Men's Hairstylist & Barber's Journal.*

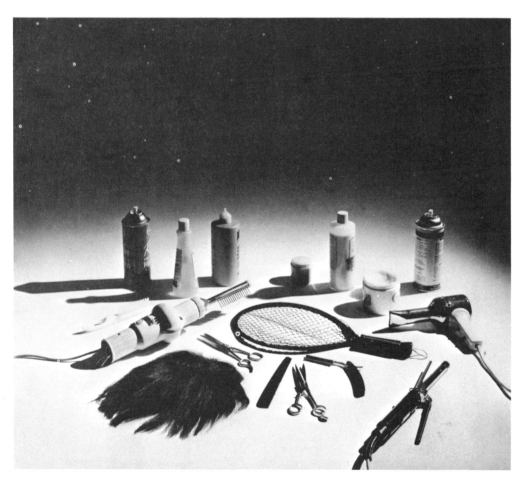

Generally speaking, there are three basic rules for basic hair care: shampoo often, brush daily, and massage regularly. In addition, if your hair is straightened, dyed, bleached, or permanented, lubricate often.

Every morning, brush your hair vigorously with a bristle brush. After brushing, spend a few minutes massaging your scalp. This will increase circulation and stimulate the natural oils. Shampoo at least once a week, or as often as needed. Whenever your hair looks dull, sticky, or greasy, it's time for another shampoo. Don't be afraid of frequent shampoos. However, be sure to use the correct shampoo for your hair type. Keep your hair in place with a hairspray. In addition, a styling gel helps control problem areas. (Ask your stylist for a complete line of grooming aids.) And most important of all, never go more than ten days or two weeks before getting another haircut. Nothing looks worse than shabby, unkempt hair.

LEFT: THE LONG, EMPIRE. Hairstyle by Roger of New York. Photo: Kenn Duncan. Courtesy of *Men's Hairstylist & Barber's Journal.*

4. Illusion Styling/Hairpieces.

Illusion styling.

If your hair is in the early stages of baldness, and isn't too far gone, illusion styling may be the answer.

Illusion styling can work wonders with receding hairlines and other balding areas. It creates the illusion of more hair by lifting the hair to its maximum fullness. Illusion styling, like any other style, begins with a shampoo and razor cut. A setting lotion is often added for body. Repeated effort with a blower and brush lifts the hair to its maximum fullness. A dash of spray completes the look.

The best part about illusion styling, is that it makes the best of what you still have. In these early stages of baldness, many men experience a feeling of self-consciousness about their particular problem. Therefore, in an effort to cover up the trouble spots, they often take it upon themselves to create some rather eccentric hairstyles. Consequently, instead of minimizing the defect, they draw attention to it.

In some cases, your hairstylist will suggest letting your hair grow in a certain way so that it can be put to better use. Follow his suggestions, and see the difference.

Instant color sprays are also helpful in camouflaging small trouble spots. After styling, a light dash of color spray may be used to eliminate that bare look. Color sprays are only temporary, and can be washed out with your next shampoo.

LEFT: ILLUSION STYLING created through the use of blower and brush. Hairstyle by Roger of New York. Photo: Lowell McFarland. Courtesy of *Men's Hairstylist & Barber's Journal.*

BEFORE

AFTER

Hairpieces

The hairpiece offers a practical solution to the problem of baldness. A hairpiece can give instant youth, and at the same time, look completely natural and non-detectable.

For the best advice on your particular problem, see your hairstylist. However, as a general guide, follow these basic rules on the care and selection of hairpieces:

• Buy the best hairpiece you can afford. Since you will be wearing your hairpiece every day, the better the quality, the longer it will last. Most men have at least two hairpieces so that they may alternate.

• Buy your hairpiece from your regular stylist. . . .a specialist in fitting, styling, and servicing. He will measure the area to be covered, make a mold, and take color samples. In addition, since you will be needing your regular haircuts, your hairstylist can tend to this at the same time that he services your hairpiece.

• If possible, buy a hairpiece in the early stages of baldness, rather than wait until your hair is practically all gone. By doing this, there will not be any radical change, and no one will ever know that you ever started to wear a hairpiece. If you start out with a small partial piece, and your condition gets progressively worse, you may add on an extension to cover the new areas of baldness.

LEFT: FALSE MOUSTACHE AND LACE-FRONT HAIRPIECE. Courtesy of Hollywood Joe's. Photos: Kenn Duncan.

TIME'S FLIGHT.

At eighteen Harry was flattered when the barber said: "Have a shave, Harry?'"

At forty-eight Henry was tickled when the barber would suggest that he have a hair-cut.

●Remember, there are hairpieces for every problem type. In general, hairpieces fall into the category of those with lace, and those without lace. Lace fronts are preferred for off-the-face styles. They look as though the hair is growing right from the scalp. You may select a lace partial, or a full lace piece, depending upon the degree of baldness. In a lace-front piece, an extension of lace is secured to the front of the head. This area may be carefully trimmed, or may be as long as 1/4" on the forehead. When it is secured with spirit gum, the lace becomes invisible.

● To secure a hairpiece, use two-sided adhesive and spirit gum. Before securing the hairpiece, make sure that your head is completely dry. Wash with soap and water, or use some cotton dipped in alcohol. Dry thoroughly.

● Know the difference between a custom-made hairpiece and a machine-made hairpiece. A custom-made hairpiece is made on a fine silk base. The hair is very closely spaced, and the strands are knotted by hand. The custom-made hairpiece is made from 100% human hair. The hair is imported from Europe, and is constructed by highly-skilled specialists. The custom-made hairpiece is blended to match the wearer's own hair, and lasts for a much longer period of time. The finished piece is completely natural and non-detectable. On the other hand, machine-made pieces, use less expensive hair, and therefore, cost less. The hair may be imported from the Orient, or it may be a special synthetic blend. Machine-made hairpieces take less time to make, and therefore, do not last as long as custom-made pieces.

LEFT: FREE, CASUAL CURLS can be reproduced through a curly stretch wig. Courtesy of Adonis For Men. Photo: Kenn Duncan.

Charles Alfieri, Inc.

BEFORE   AFTER

• To find out whether a hairpiece contains 100% human hair, or synthetic fibres, follow this easy test: Take a few sample hairs from the hairpiece and burn with a match. If the hairpiece is made from human hair, the hair will burn slowly and give off an odor of chicken feathers. Synthetic hair burns more rapidly, and practically has no odor.

• Styling is extremely important in men's hairpieces. Even if you use the best hair possible, if it is not properly styled, the hairpiece will not look natural. Remember, if you're 40 years old, don't expect to have the same hairline that you had when you were 20 years old. Depend upon your stylist's good judgement.

• Hairpieces come in an infinite variety of styles. There are hairpieces to correspond with every hairstyle. For example, there are Empire or Caesar Cuts, Pompadours, and off-the-face styles, Madison Avenue and Ivy League styles, etc. In addition, there are small partial fill-ins for receding hairlines, partial crown pieces the size of a coin, full-fashioned pieces with built-in sideburns, inexpensive stretch wigs, and a variety of other styles. The size of a hairpiece may vary from a 1" partial in the back of the head, to a hairpiece which covers the entire head. Whatever the problem, there is a hairpiece to correct it.

LEFT: LACE-FRONT HAIRPIECE. Hairpiece by Michael Yaccarino. Photo: Kenn Duncan. Courtesy of *Men's Hairstylist & Barber's Journal.*

HAIR WEAVING

5. Hair Weaving/Hair Transplanting
Hair Weaving

Hair weaving is the process of adding hair to your own existing hair. The process, which takes approximately four hours to complete, involves taking up strands of your own hair and making a foundation. The base is a mixture of your own hair and 100% European hair, which is interwoven with thread. Hair weaving costs from $200 to $400, depending upon the area to be covered, and the type of hair required.

The basic technique involves wearing a base of silk thread, putting down the tracks, sewing the wefting onto the tracks, and styling the hair. Adjustments of tightenings are usually necessary every six to eight weeks, depending upon the rate of growth. The cost of adjustments varies considerably. Some methods which require only five to ten minutes of adjustment cost only $5 to $10 per tightening. Other methods, which involve several hours of work, cost as much as $25 to $50 per tightening.

The amount of hair needed for hair weaving varies. Once again, it depends upon the method used. Although some methods require 40% of the natural hair, other methods require only a very small, light fringe of hair over the ears and around the back of the head.

Hair weaving, if done by a competent professional, gives a completely natural look. Since the hair does not come off, the hair will act like a natural head of hair. The hair will look messed up when the client awakens, will blow naturally when exposed to the wind, and if it is properly treated, can be washed and shampooed like your own hair.

LEFT: AFTER HAIRWEAVING. Photo: Lowell McFarland (Courtesy of *Men's Hairstylist & Barber's Journal*).

Hair weaving is suitable for the early stages of baldness when a man is experiencing his first loss of hair. With hair weaving, the client can fill in the thinning areas, and continue to do so, should the condition get progressively worse. Hair weaving is also suitable for the more advanced stages of baldness. However, since not all methods are alike, the amount of hair required varies. Note: If you are considering hair weaving, be sure to consult a reputable company. If it is not done properly, you may be confronted with headaches, loss of hair, etc.

Hair Transplanting

Hair transplanting is a surgical operation achieved by means of skin grafts. Each transplant costs from $5 to $25 a graft, depending upon the doctor used. A man with a receding hairline may need as many as 200 transplants. A man with a greater degree of baldness needs about 300 transplants.

At each session, the doctor takes plugs containing about 6 to 12 hairs from the back to the front. The scalp, of course, is anesthetized at each session. A doctor can do approximately 15 grafts at one session. Eventually, the doctor replaces the front vacancies with the hirsute plugs.

After the initial operation, a crust develops on the surface of the transplanted area. The crust falls away in about two to three weeks. In about two to eight weeks, the hair stubs in the transplants fall out. It takes about 12 weeks before the new growth of hair appears. The new hair, although it may not be as full as a hairpiece, looks natural and can be easily styled.

LEFT: THIS FULL, CASUAL STYLE created with a body wave, can be duplicated with either a hi-fashion stretch wig or a Combo-Weave, which is a hairpiece woven onto the head. Hairstyle by Michael Yaccarino. Courtesy of *Men's Hairstylist & Barber's Journal.*

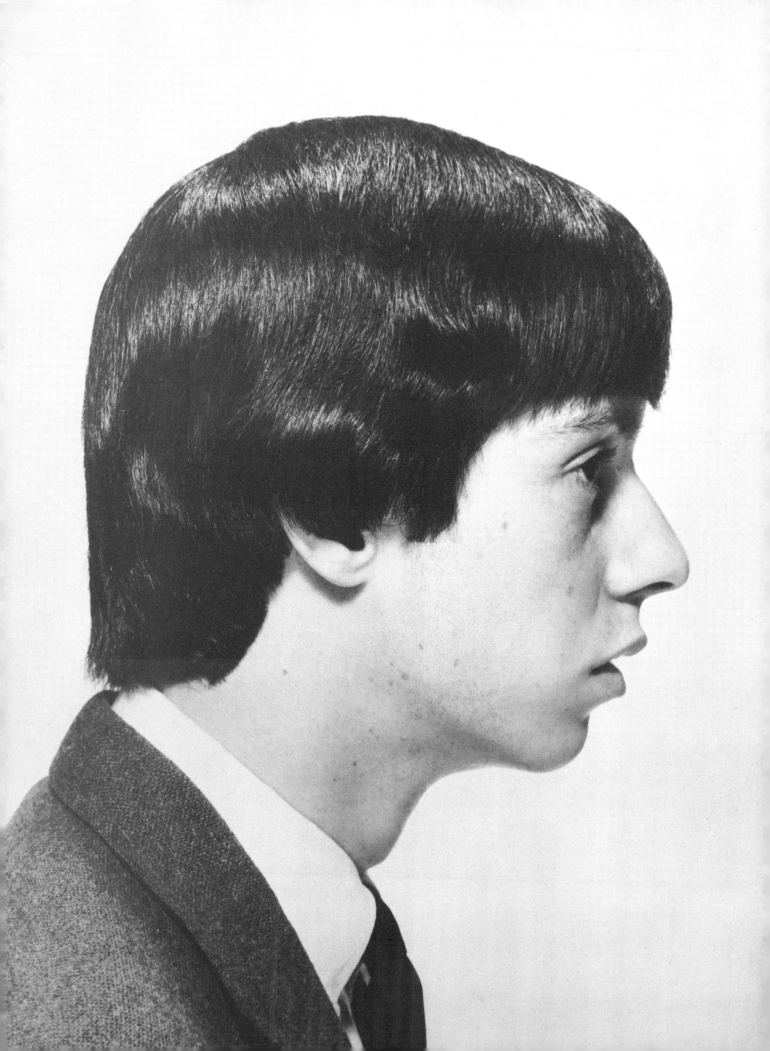

6. Hair Straightening/Permanent Waving
Hair Straightening

Curly or wavy hair can really be a problem for some men. This type hair has a mind of its own, and is usually difficult-to-handle. The curls or waves may be in only one area, or throughout the entire head. In either case, the styling possibilities are limited.

To offer more flexibility, many hairstylists recommend hair straightening. This process, which is also known as hair relaxing, makes the hair smooth and manageable. It lasts anywhere from one month to two months, depending upon the rate of growth. It is semi-permanent, and does not shampoo out.

What happens when you get your hair straightened is a relatively easy process. First, your scalp and skin is protected with a coating of petroleum jelly. A cream straightener is applied to the hair, and later combed through it. The processor softens the curl. After your hair is rinsed out in lukewarm water, a stabilizer keeps the hair in a relaxed position. A cream rinse or conditioner usually follows.

Hair straightening should never be a do-it-yourself project. It requires professional know-how. Left in the hands of an amateur, hair straightening can lead to serious damage of the hair and scalp.

Do not attempt hair straightening unless your hair is in excellent condition. Avoid hair straightening if your scalp is extremely sensitive, or your hair has been badly damaged from overprocessed dyes or permanents. In addition, if you have any open cuts, abrasions, or infections, postpone hair straightening until these areas heal.

Since hair straightening can be drying to the hair, regular conditioning treatments are recommended. These treatments will replenish the natural oils which are lost during straightening.

LEFT: AFTER HAIRSTRAIGHTENING. Hairstraightening by Joseph Dixey. Photo: Kenn Duncan (Courtesy of *Men's Hairstylist & Barber's Journal*).

THE BODY WAVE FOR FINE, THINNING HAIR.

Permanent waving

Fine, limp hair, as well as thinning hair, often benefits from a permanent wave.

If the permanent is give purely for body, it is usually called a body wave. A body wave has no apparent curls or waves, only hidden body. It gives limp hair a foundation, and creates the illusion of fullness. Since the hair is short, only a few rods are necessary. The hair is first softened with a chemical solution which makes the hair receptive to change. The hair is then rolled on special rods. A neutralizer locks in the body. A body wave takes about one hour and lasts anywhere from four weeks to two months.

Body waves are also available without rods. Body-building qualities are shampooed into the hair. The body is locked in with a neutralizer.

LEFT: THE CURLY, GRECIAN LOOK. Hairstyle by Roger of New York. Photo: Kenn Duncan. Courtesy of Men's Hairstylist & Barber's Journal.

For short, curly hairstyles, regular permanent waves are recommended. The degree of curliness is determined by the kind of solution used, the size of the rods, and the texture of the hair.

Once again, permanent waving is not for amateurs. The waves do not shampoo out, therefore, there is no room for error. Besides, overprocessing can cause considerable damage to your hair and scalp.

To counteract dryness, make frequent use of conditioners.

LEFT: CURLY HAIR, as seen on the Head of David.

7. Hair Coloring: Temporary, Semi-Permanent, and Permanent

Hair coloring should never be a do-it-yourself project. On the contrary, this is one process which requires professional know-how.

First of all, before hair coloring, a thorough examination of the hair and scalp is necessary. If any open cuts, abrasions, or infections are visible, the haircoloring must be postponed until these conditions are corrected. Secondly, to prevent against any allergic reactions, a patch test must be given 24 hours prior to the actual coloring.

Today's market offers a variety of different coloring agents, designed specifically for men. For example, there are temporary rinses, semi-permanent colorings, and of course, permanent colorings. A temporary coloring highlights the hair and washes out with the next shampoo. A semi-permanent hair coloring covers and blends, and usually lasts about five times as long as temporary colorings. A permanent hair coloring, of course, lasts until the hair grows out.

Always keep in mind that a man's hair color must compliment his age and skin tones. For example, an elderly man, because of the soft effect which white hair may have on his features, would probably look better if he kept his hair natural. Rather than hide the grey, he should emphasize it with either a temporary or semi-permanent hair coloring. Usually, a blue rinse is all that is needed to tone down unwanted yellows. On the other hand, should this same man suddenly turn from white hair to black hair, the overall effect would be entirely too harsh, especially if his skin tones reflected his true age.

LEFT: GREY HAIR which has been highlighted with a semi-permanent rinse. Hairstyle by Roger of New York. Photo: Kenn Duncan. (Courtesy of *Men's Hairstylist & Barber's Journal*).

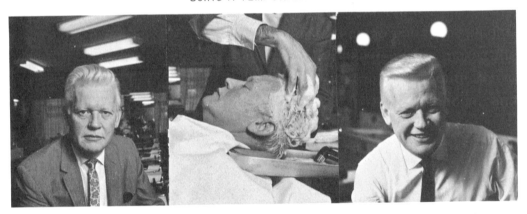

However, the middle-aged man has another alternative. If he is partially grey, and wishes to color his hair because age is becoming a problem, by all means, he should do so. A soft brown would probably enhance his skin tones, and make him look years younger. If he has grey sideburns, he would probably be better off keeping them, for a more natural effect.

The younger man, with premature grey hair, of course, has the greatest flexibility. By using just a steel-grey rinse or semi-permanent coloring, he can highlight and blend his hair. As long as his skin tones are young, the grey hair will probably not detract from his youthful appearance. On the contrary, it often gives the younger man a look of distinction. For a complete change of color, a soft permanent or semi-permanent hair color is recommended.

Psychologically speaking, temporary and semi-permanent colorings, are recommended for those men who still have some qualms about coloring. These colorings usually lead the way to permanent hair coloring. Permanent hair coloring is perfect for the man who has no doubts. It offers the greatest variety of shades, and if done professionally, looks very natural. Retouching is required every two to three weeks.

For special effects, such as sun-streaking or frosting, pre-bleaching is necessary. Special lighteners are used for these unusual effects. In frosting, a special perforated cap is used, so that various strands of hair may be lightened over the head. Sun-streaking is usually done at the front hairline.

LEFT: HIGHLIGHTING GREY HAIR WITH A TEMPORARY COLOR RINSE. Hairstyle by Roger of New York. Photo: Kenn Duncan. Courtesy of *Men's Hairstylist & Barber's Journal.*

8. Men's Cosmetics And Skin Care

Both men and women are subject to the same skin problems: ageing, bad weather, and artificial heating. Therefore, men's cosmetics are needed to cleanse, to correct, to condition. If a man's skin is not kept clean, dirt, scales, and oil will clog the pores and create skin problems. In addition, this condition will hinder the normal respiration of the skin.

Skin treatment starts with a shave. Blemished skins can be followed up with a medicated cover-up. Stubborn beards can be softened with special beard softeners. Extra-sensitive skins will respond to rich, smoothing emollients.

Make-up, that is, a basic foundation, can be used to even out skin tones, disguise a heavy beard, or cover up minor blemishes. Cake talcs, which add color to the skin, create a natural, matte finish. Bronzing gels, in natural shades, give coverage without a made-up look. Make-up sticks in lighter shades than the basic foundation, disguise five o'clock shadow and minor blemishes.

Regular facials should be included in a man's skin care program. A facial, which can mean anything from a facial massage to a facial skin treatment, tones, relaxes, stimulates, cleanses, and protects. In addition, moisturizers combat wrinkles. Astringents tighten pores. Mud packs improve skin tones.

LEFT: CAKE TALC, as worn for businesswear. Photo: Lowell McFarland. Courtesy of *Men's Hairstylist & Barber's Journal.*

ANALYZING SKIN PROBLEMS   THE FACIAL

Normal skin is neither too dry, nor too oily. It is usually blemish-free and smooth-textured. However, if you have a normal, healthy skin, do not take it for granted. Over-exposure to sun, cold, and wind will eventually abuse it. To combat future problems, use cold weather creams and moisturizers.

Dry skin is usually patchy and taut. It has fine lines and feels almost parched. Avoid strong soaps and astringent lotions. Use an all purpose emollient for daily cleansing. Regular dry skin facials and special sun and sports creams will add moisture and lubrication to dry areas.

Oily skin has a shiny, greasy appearance. It usually has large pores, blackheads, and pimples. Avoid fatty cleansing creams. Use astringents which shrink the pores and a medicated soap for regular cleansing. Treat yourself to a special oily skin facial regularly.

Combination skin, that is, skin which has both dry and oily areas, requires double care. The oily areas are usually found around the nose, chin, and forehead. The temples, cheeks, and eye areas are usually dry. Each area must be treated separately. The dry areas will need rich lubricants. The oily areas will need astringent cleansers.

LEFT: BRONZING GEL for the active, outdoor look. Photo: Lowell McFarland. Courtesy of *Men's Hairstylist & Barber's Journal.*

FROM GERMANY: ZDF/IRM   FROM SWEDEN: Svenska Frisortidningen

9. Portfolio Of Styles (International Showcase)

Credit is given to the following picture sources: Pages 235 and 236, Hollywood Joe's; Page 51, Gift of John D. Rockefeller, Jr., 1931, The Metropolitan Museum of Art, Page 62, Purchase 1966, The Metropolitan Museum of Art, Page 86, Page 92, The Jules S. Bache Collection, 1949, The Metropolitan Museum of Art, Page 119, Gift of H. O. Havemeyer, The Metropolitan Museum of Art, Page 119 painted for Daniel Carroll, The Metropolitan Museum of Art, Page 162, Copyrighted and registered by The Journeymen Barbers' Union, Page 164, R. Taylor, Page 239, Charles Alfieri, Inc., Page 237, Adonis For Men, Page 181, Ed Pinaud.

Grateful acknowledgement is also given to the following sources: Pages 207, Hollywood Joe's; Page 182, Rockefeller Center; Page 23 , Fernando Del Campo; Page 111, Dresden Galerie; Page 119, The Metropolitan Museum of Art; Pages 67, 95, 180, 220, 221, 222, 225, 227, 233, 249, and 251, *Men's Hairstylist & Barber's Journal;* Page 241, Original Hair Weavers.

Pages 263, 265, and 271 are reproduced through the courtesy of *Hair & Beauty.* All other style photos are reproduced through the courtesy of *Men's Hairstylist & Barber's Journal,* unless otherwise noted.

Illustrations on Pages 4, 10, 12, 108, 112, 116, 118, 124, 128, 130, 132, 155, 156, and 159, are reproduced through the courtesy of the New York Public Library Print Division.

All movie photos were selected from the Gene Andrewski collection. Grateful acknowledgement is given to all the studios involved, such as, Warner Bros., Twentieth Century Fox, Universal, MGM, etc.

Illustrations on pages 175, 177, and 180 are reproduced through the courtesy of *Men's Hairstylist & Barber's Journal.* Page 223 is reproduced through the courtesy of *Hollywood Joe's.*

Many of the photos reproduced in this book were taken from the authors' private collection. In addition, although all attempts were made to credit the proper sources, we regret any oversights which may have been made.

LEFT: From Japan — Seichi Seo.

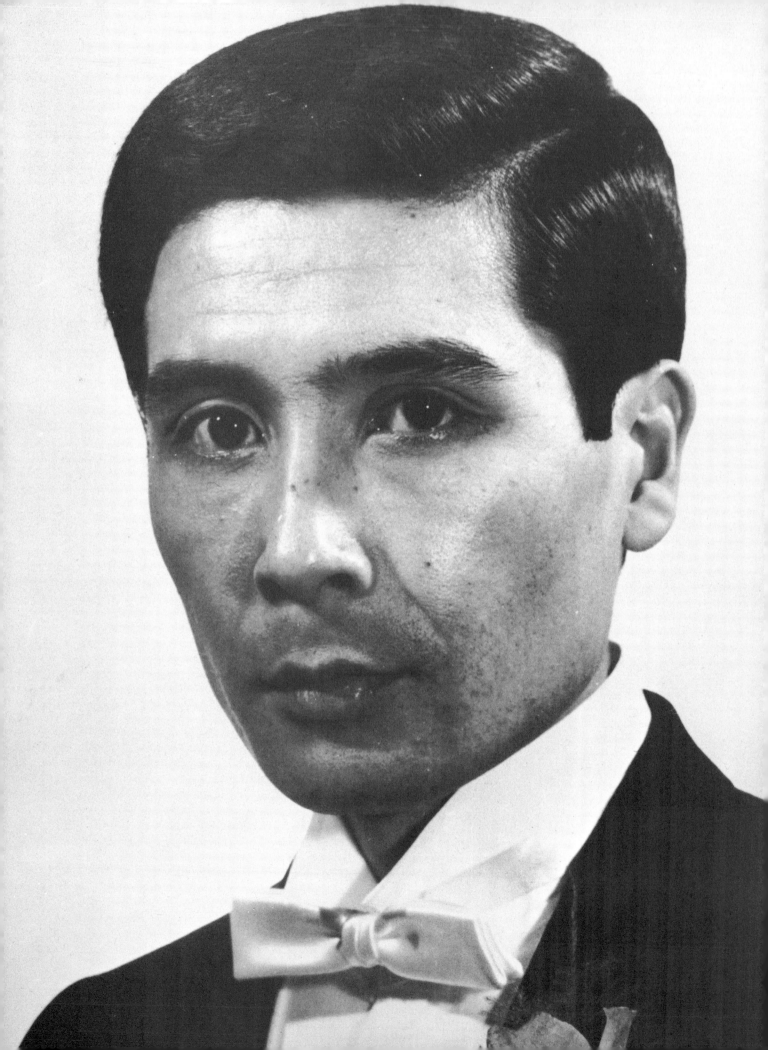

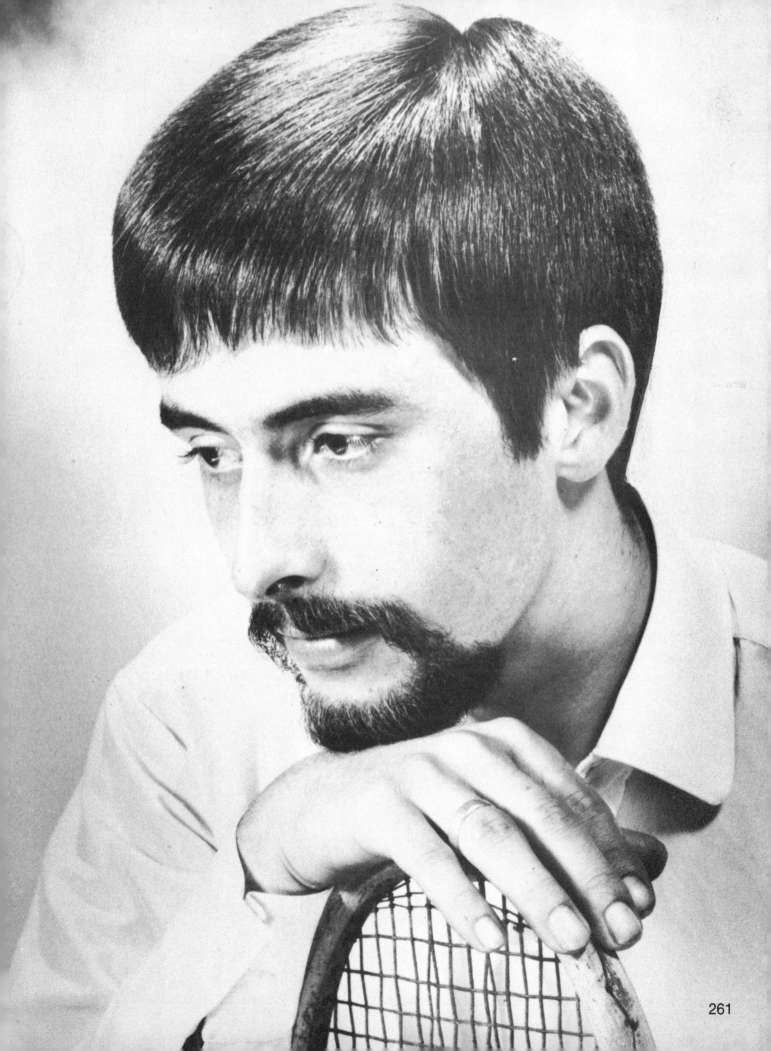

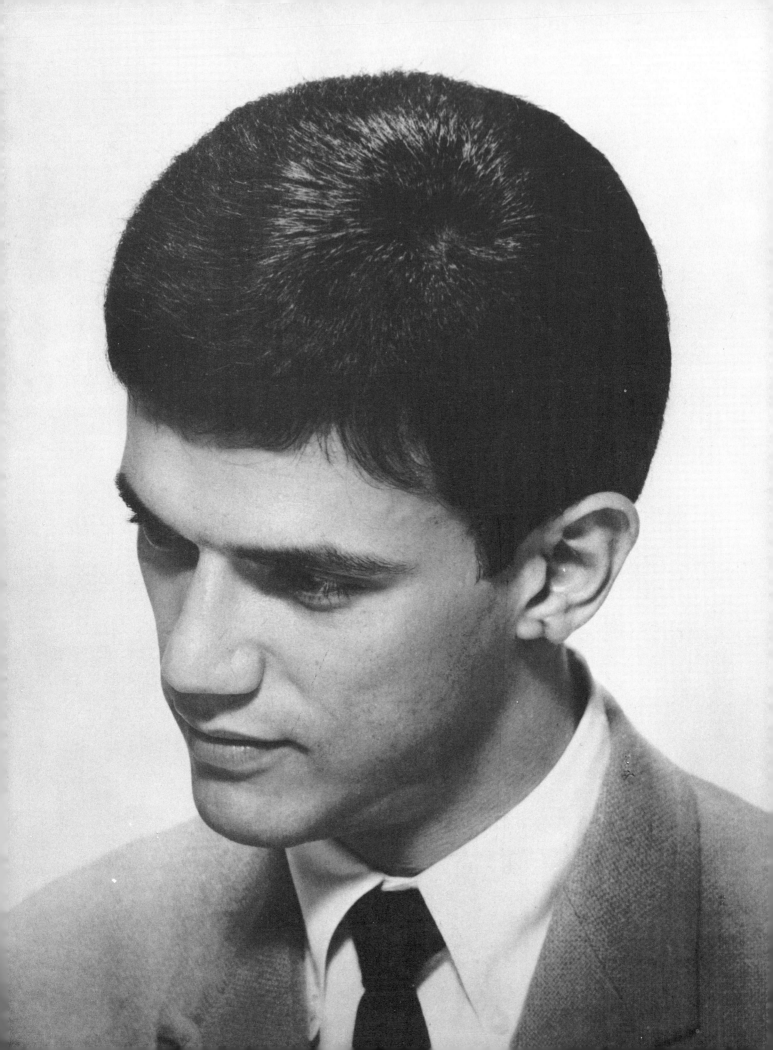

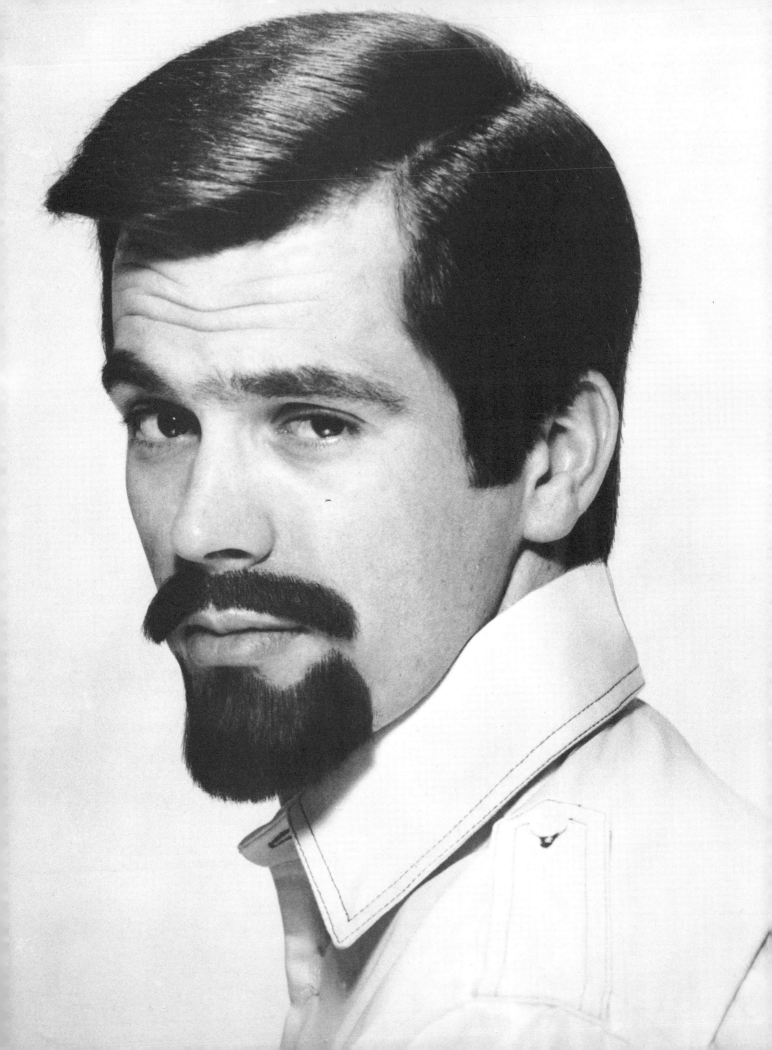

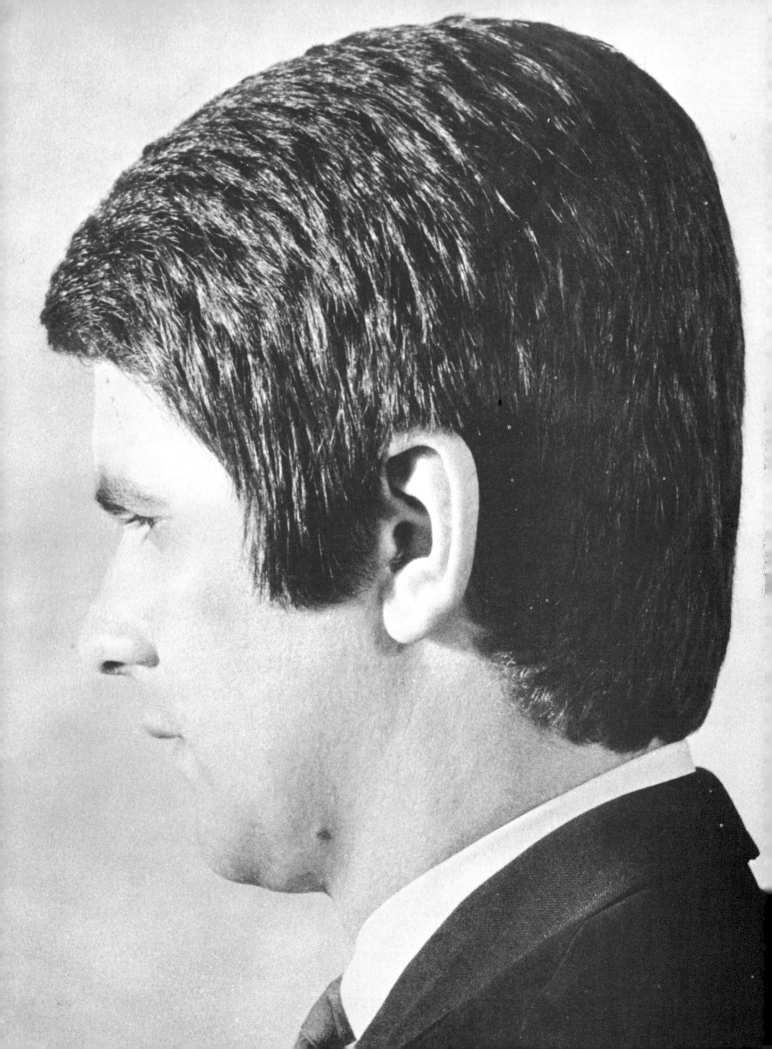

BIBLIOGRAPHY

Abrahams, Ethel B.—*Greek Dress;* John Murray, London, 1908.

Allen, Agnes—*The Story of Clothes;* Faber & Faber, London, 1955.

Allen & Ticknor—*The Toilette of Health, Beauty, & Fashion, embracing the economy of the beard, moustache, etc. with a variety of select recipes for the dressing room of both sexes;* Boston, 1833.

Andrews, William—*At the Sign of the Barber's Pole;* J.R. Tutin, Cottingham, Yorkshire, 1904.

Ashdown, Charles H. (Mrs.)—*British Costume During XIV Centuries;* Thomas Nelson & Sons, Ltd., London, New York.

Asser, Joyce—*Historic Hairdressing;* Sir Isaac Pitman & Sons, Ltd., London, 1966.

Barton, Lucy—*Historic Costume For The Stage;* Walter H. Baker Company, Boston, 1935.

Beerbohm, Max—*A Defense of Cosmetics;* Dodd, Mead & Company, New York, 1922.

Begy, Joseph A.—*Practical Handbook of Toilet Preparations;* William L. Allison, New York, 1889.

Bergler, Edmund—*Fashion And The Unconscious;* Robert Brunner, New York, 1953.

Binder, Pearl—*Muffs And Morals;* George G. Harrap & Company, Ltd., Great Britain, 1953.

Binder, Pearl—*The Peacock's Tail;* George G. Harrap & Company, Ltd., Toronto and Great Britain, 1958.

Birmingham, Frederick A. —*Esquire Fashion Guide For All Occasions;* Harper & Brothers, New York.

Boucher, Francois—*20,000 Years of Fashion; The History of Costume And Personal Adornment;* Harry N. Abrams, Inc., New York, 1967.

Bowser, Milton—*Safe Chemical Hair Straightening;* The Washington Company, Pittsburg, 1966.

Bradley, H. Dennis—*The Eternal Masquerade;* T. Werner Laurie, Ltd., London, 1922.

Brooke, Iris—*Dress And Undress*—The Restoration and Eighteenth Century; Methuen & Company, Ltd., London, 1958.

Brummel, George Bryan (Beau)—*Male And Female Costume;* Illustrated From The Manuscript, Edited, and With An Introduction by Eleanor Parker, Doubleday, Doran & Company, Inc., New York, 1932.

Brunialti, A.—*Popoli del Mondo Usi E Costumi Africa, Vol.1, Vol. 2;* Milan, 1880.

Camerale, Stamperia - *Addizioni Agli Statuti Delle Arti Di Barbiere e Perucchiere;* Bologna, 1719.

Carcopino, Jerome - *Daily Life In Ancient Rome;* Yale University Press, 1940.

Carr, Lucien - *Dress & Ornaments of Certain American Indians;* Charles Hamilton, Worcester, Mass., 1897.

Cazenane, Dr. A. - *The Art of Human Decoration*; Paris, 1874.

Chambers' Encyclopedia, 1967.

Christy, R.—*Proverbs, Maxims and Phrases of All Ages*; New York,1907.

Clodd, Edward - *The Childhood of the World*; Kegan, Paul, Trench, Trubner & Company, London, 1893.

Collier's Encyclopedia, 1968.

Connoisseur Period Guides, The Stuart Period 1603-1714; London, 1957.

Connoisseur Period Guides, The Regency Period, 1810-1830: London, 1958.

Connoisseur Period Guides, The Early Victorian Period, 1830-1860: London, 1958.

Cooley, Arthur J.—*Cosmetics, And Perfumes And Other Toilet Articles;* Robert Hardwicke, 1868.

Cooley, Arthur J.—*Toilet In Ancient And Modern Times;* 1873.

Corson, Richard—*Fashions In Hair;* Peter Owens, Ltd., 1965.

Cottrell, Kent—*Sunburnt Sketches of Africa, South, East & West;* Central News Agency, Ltd. 1953.

Cottrell, Leonard—*Life Under The Pharoahs;* Evans Bros. Ltd., London, 1955.

Cox, J. Stevens—*An Illustrated Dictionary of Hairdressing and Wigmaking;* George S. MacManus Company, Philadelphia, 1966.

Cunnington. C. W. and Phillis—*Handbook of English Mediaeval Costume; Handbook of English Costume In The Sixteenth Century;* Faber & Faber, London.

DeGiafferi, Paul Louis—*History of French Masculine Costume, Volume I—Volume VI;* Foreign Publications, New York.

DeKock, Charles Paul—*The Barber of Paris;* The C. F. Brainard Publishing Company, 1903.

Donelan, Daniel—*Figaro . . . In All Ages;* The Varriale Publication, New York, 1927.

Dupeyrat, Andre—*Savage Papua;* E. P. Dutton & Company, New York, 1954.

Dyer, E. R. —*Hairdresser's Technical Encyclopedia;* London, 1949.

Earl, George Windsor—*The Native Races or The Indian Archipelago, Papuans;* London, 1853.

Eichler, Nelson—*The Customs of Mankind;* Doubleday, Inc., New York, 1924.

Encyclopedia Americana, 1969.

Encyclopedia Brittanica, 1969.

Evans, Bergen—*Dictionary of Quotations;* New York, 1968.

Evans, Joan—*Dress In Mediaeval France;* The Clarendon Press, Oxford, 1952.

Foan, Gilbert A.—*The Art & Craft of Hairdressing;* Sir Isaac Pitman & Sons, Ltd., London, 1936.

Forbes, Evelyn—*Hairdressing And Beauty As A Career;* B. J. Batsford, London, 1961.

Funk & Wagnalls New Standard Dictionary of The English Language; 1969.

Gardner, Ernest Arthur—*Ancient Athens;* Macmillan Company, New York, 1902.

Gernsheim, Alison—*Fashion And Reality;* Faber & Faber, London, 1963.

Gill, Eric—*Clothes;* Jonathan Cape, London, 1931.

Goodman, Herman—*Your Hair. Its Health, Beauty, and Growth;* Emerson Books, 1950.

Gorsline, Douglas—*What People Wore;* The Viking Press, 1952.

Gould, Grace Margaret—*The Magic of Dress;* Doubleday, Page & Company, New York, 1911.

Gross, Otto— *Deutsche Barbier, Friseur und Perucken Macher;* 1904.

Hairdresser's Chronicle; 1872.

Hairdresser's Weekly Journal; 1882.

Hall, S. Roland—*The Advertising Handbook;* McGraw-Hill Book, New York, 1930.

Hartley, Cecil B.—*The Gentlemen's Book of Etiquette;* Boston, 1860.

Haweis, H. R. (Mrs.)—*The Art of Beauty;* Harper & Bros., New York 1878.

Haweis, H. R. (Mrs.)—*The Art of Dress;* Chalto & Windus, London, 1879.

Hawes, Elizabeth—*It's Still Spinach;* Little, Brown & Company, New York, 1952.

Hawes, Elizabeth—*Men Can Take It!;* Random House, New York, 1939.

Heard, Gerald—*Narcissus—An Anatomy of Clothes;* Kegan, Paul, Trench, Trubner & Company, London and New York, E. P. Dutton, 1924.

Hiler, Hilaire—*From Nudity To Rainment;* The Educational Press, New York, 1930.

Hoey, Cashel (Mrs.)—*Yester-Year—Ten Centuries of Toilette;* From the French of A. Robida, Charles Scribner's Sons, New York, 1891.

"Homo Sum"—*The Science of Shaving;* W. Heffer & Sons, Ltd., 1931.

Horning, Clarence—*Handbook of Early Advertising Art,* Dover Publications, New York.

Houston, Mary G. and Florence S. Hornblower—*Ancient Egyptian, Assyrian and Persian Costumes and Decorations;* A.C. Black, Ltd., London, 1920.

Houston, Mary G.—*Ancient Greek, Roman & Byzantine Costume;* A & C Black, Ltd., London, 1931.

Houston, Mary G.—*Medieval Costume In England and France;* Adam & Charles Black, London, 1939.

Jones, Edgar R.—*Those Were The Gool Old Days—A Happy look At American Advertising, 1880-1930;* Simon & Shuster, New York, 1959.

Keith, Arthur—*Ancient Types of Man;* Harper & Brothers, London and New York, 1911.

Kelly, Francis M. and Randolph Schwabe—*A Short History of Costume And Armour (1066-1485);* Scribners, New York and London, 1931.

Kohler, Carl—*A History of Costume;* Philadelphia, 1920.

L'Illustration de la Coiffure.

La Coiffure Francaise Illustree, 1925.

La Coiffure et Les Modes, 1918-1932.

LaCroix, Paul—*Histoire de la Coiffure et de la barbe;* Paris, 1851.

LaFoy, J. B. M. D.—*The Complete Coiffeur. An Essay On The Art of Adorning Natural And of Creating Artificial Beauty;* New York, 1817.

La Mode A Paris; 1930.

Langner, Lawrence—*The Importance of Wearing Clothes;* Hastings House, New York, 1959.

La Toilette; 1898.

Laver, James—*Clothes;* Horizontal Press, New York, 1953.

Laver, James—*Dress;* John Murray, London, 1950 *(The Changing Shape of Things Series).*

Laver, James—*Style In Costume;* Oxford University Press, 1949.

Ledoux, Hector and Elie Etienne—*Le Parfait Salonnier—Methode Pratique de Coiffure Masculine;* Paris, 1926.

Le Coiffeur Europeen; 1874.

Le Moniteur de la Coiffure; 1867.

Lester, Katherine Morris and Bess Viola Oerke—*An Illustrated History of Those Frills and Furbellows of Fashion Which Have Come To Be Known As Accessories of Dress;* The Manual Arts Press, Peoria, Ill.

Lubowe, Irwin I. and Barbara Huss—*A Teen-Age Guide To Healthy Skin and Hair;* E. P. Dutton & Company, Inc., New York, 1965.

Lubowe, Irwin I.—*New Hope For Your Hair;* E. P. Dutton & Company, Inc., New York, 1960.

"Major" of To-Day—*Clothes And The Man;* M. F. Mansfield, London, Grant Richards, 1900s.

Mantegagazza—*Tartuffian Age;* 1800.

Marneffe, Alph. de—*Les Cheveux, La Barbe Et La Moustache A Travers Les Ages;* 1939.

Men's Hairstylist & Barber's Journal.

Mercado, Frank—*The Barber's Philosophy And His Art;* 1966.

Metropolitan Museum of Art Catalogue of French Paintings XV—XVII; Charles Sterling Harvard University Press, Cambridge, 1955, *Vol. 1, Vol. 2—XIV Century—XIX Century.*

Mitchell, Edwin Valentine—*Concerning Beards;* Dodd, Mead and Company, New York, 1930.

Montez, Madame Lola—*The Arts of Beauty or Secrets of a Lady's Toilete With Hints To Gentlemen on The Art of Fascination;* Dick & Fitzgerald, New York, 1858.

Moler, A. B.—*The Barber's Manual;* Chicago, 1911.

New York Public Library (Art Division); *Scrapbook on Costume Accessories.*

Norris, Herbert—*Costume and Fashion—The Evolution of European Dress Thru the Earlier Ages;* J. M. Dent & Sons, London, 1924, New York, E. P. Dutton & Company.

Norris, Herbert—*Costume & Fashion, Vol. 3—The Tudors—Book I (1485—1547),* J. M. Dent, 1938, E. P. Dutton, New York.

Norris, Herbert—*Costume And Fashion—Vol. 3—The Tudors— Book II (1547—1603)*, J. M. Dent & Sons, 1938, E. P. Dutton, New York.

One of the Ladies' Committee of Almanacks—*How To Arrange The Hair;* Partridge & Company, London, 1857.

Parrotto, Anthony J.—*Baldness, Grayness, Dandruff—Treatable or Nontreatable;* Whitmore Publishing, Philadelphia, 1961.

Parsons, Frank Alvah—*The Psychology of Dress;* Doubleday, Page and Company, New York, 1920.

Payne, Blanche—*History of Costume, From The Ancient Egyptians To The Twentieth Century;* Harper& Row, New York, 1965.

Perret, J. J.—*La Pogonatomie;* Paris, 1700s.

Piesse—*The Art of Perfumery;* 1855.

Power, Susan C. (Mrs.)—*The Ugly-Girl Papers Or Hints For The Toilet;* Harper and Bros., New York, 1875.

Price, N. P.—*When Men Wore Muffs;* J. M. Dent & Sons, Ltd., London, 1936.

Presbrey, Frank—*The History And Development of Advertising;* Doubleday, Doran & Company, Inc., New York, 1929.

Procter, Richard Wright—*The Barber's Shop;* Simpkin, Marshall & Company, London, 1883.

Reader's Guide To Periodical Literature; 1966-1967.

Redgrave, H. Stanley and Gilbert A. Foan—*Blonde or Brunette?;* London, 1929.

Reynolds, Reginald—*Beards;* Doubleday & Company, Inc., 1949.

Rosenthal—*Pertaining To Costume.*

Rowland, Alexander—*The Human Hair;* Piper Bros., London, 1853.

Robinson, E. M.—*Illustrated Book Of Instruction on the Art of Barbering, Massaging and Kindred Subjects;* Spokane, Washington, 1906.

Smith, Adelaide and Reuben Rockwood—*Modern Beauty and Barber Science;* Prentice Hall, 1931.

Smithsonian Institute—*Smithsonian Miscellaneous Collections,* Vol. 85; 1933.

Society For The Advancement of Hair And Beauty Science—*Hair & Beauty Science;* 1928.

Speight, Alexanna—*The Lock of Hair;* London, 1871.

Steiner, Gerald—*Crowning Glory;* Gerald Buckworth & Company, Ltd., London, 1955.

Story, Margaret—*Individuality And Clothes;* Funk & Wagnalls, New York and London, 1930.

Square Deal.

Seton, Julia M.—*The Indian Costume Book;* The Seton Village Press; Santa Fe and New York, 1938.

Textbook Committee of Barbering—*Advanced Textbook of Barbering and Men's Hairstyling;* Milady Publishing Corporation, New York, 1969.

Thurston, Joseph—*The Toilette In Three Books;* London, 1730.

Truman, Nevil—*Historic Costuming;* Sir Isaac Pitman & Sons, Ltd., London, 1936.

Trusty L. Sherman—*The Art & Science of Barbering, Revised Edition;* U.S.A., 1962.

Turner, E. S.—*The Shocking History of Advertising;* E. P. Dutton & Company, New York, 1953.

Twigg, Phyllis—*A Little Booke of Conceited Secrets and Delights For Ladies;* London, 1928.

Uberden Gebrauch—*Falchen haare und perructen;* Berlin, 1801.

Vail, Gilbert—*A History of Cosmetics In America;* Prepared by The Toilet Goods Association, New York.

VonBoehn, Max—*Modes And Manners;Vol. I—From The Decline of The Ancient World To The Renaissance, Vol. II—The Sixteenth Century, Vol. III—The Seventeenth Century, Vol. IV—The Eighteenth Century;* J. B. Lippincott Company, Philadelphia, 1932.

Vogel, Alfred A.—*Papuans & Pygmies;* Arthur Baker, Ltd., 1953.

Wadleigh, R. H.—*Head Gear—Antique and Modern;* Coleman and Maxwell, Boston, 1879.

Walker, Alexander—*The Book of Beauty With Modes For Improving and Preserving It In Man And Woman;* Holland and Glover, 1843.

Walker, Isaac—*Dress—As It Has Been, Is, And Will Be;* New York, 1885.

Walkup, Fairfax—*Dressing The Part;* Appleton-Century Crofts, Inc., 1950.

Warwick, Edward and Henry C. Fitz—*Early American Costume;* The Century Company, New York, 1929.

Webb, Wilfred Mark—*The Heritage of Dress;* The Times Book Club, London, 1912.

Welford and Armstrong—*Art In Ornament and Dress;* Scribner, New York, 1877.

Wilcox, N. Turner—*The Mode In Hats And Headdress;* Charles Scribner, New York and London, 1959.

Wilcox, R. Turner—*Five Centuries of American Costume;* Charles Scribner, New York, 1963.

Wilkinson, Sir J. Gardner; *The Ancient Egyptians;* John Murray, London, 1854.

Wykes, Max and Joyce—*Cosmetics And Adornment;* Philosophical Library, New York, 1961.

World Book Encyclopedia; 1966.

Young, Sidney—*Annals of the Barber Surgeons;* Blades East and Blades, London, 1890.

Zemler, Charles de—*Once over Lightly;* U. S. A., 1939.

Zucker, Irving—*A Source Book of French Advertising Art;* George Braziller, 1964.

CHILDHOOD.   YOUTH.   MANHOOD.   MIDDLE LIFE.   AGE.

Conclusion

Do not be deterred by the Boston Transcript, nor by any other doubtful authority, that tells you two years of an old man's life is wasted by attending the hairdresser's shop—that the wearing of your beard will keep you out of many a painful scrape—and that the cost of shaving would build you an ornamental college. Ornamental nonsense. Walk in frankly and often. Accept the invitation of the pole. Think of Marc Anthony, who got himself barbered 10 times over before going to feast with Cleopatra, the voluptuous dark-eyed Queen of Egypt. Think, too, of Moliere, the wittiest of French wits, and the long visits he used to pay to his cherished friend, the frizeur of Pezenas. The genial atmosphere and pleasant chat of the place will not only enliven the passing hour, but will lengthen out your days to such an extent that a year or two, more or less, will never be missed.—The Barber's Shop, 1883.

LEFT: A VICTORIAN BARBER SHOP. Courtesy of Rockefeller Center, Inc.